THE PATHWAYS OF THE HEART

VANESSA SINCLAIR

TRAPART*books*

Vanessa Sinclair *The Pathways of the Heart*

Trapart Books 2021
ISBN 978-91-986919-3-1

Trapart Books
P.O. Box 8105
SE-104 20 Stockholm
Sweden

info@trapart.net
www.trapart.net
www.patreon.com/vanessa23carl

RITUAL

Her is the last of the vision fion a beginning of truth

ass: Miss Teenage America was stoned, gla

that conveys a sensuous sense of certainty

apparatus that allows me to reminisce!

grass or the scalding tops of parked cars.

action was tuned to a conscious attempt to disseminate this vision.

This in some measure explains the development of his early ar
which would be particularly great in a baby who had a

annihilation, must also expect to experience the dissolution of
himself. "The sharpness of wisdom turns upon the sage: wisd
crime against nature": such are the terrible expressions the myt

and wiggling her butt in the entranceways.

colour and texture. In the darkness all cats

God was a bit of

ultimately failed agent provocat

4

Call me Madam

Except patients suffering from
we cannot keep them for long,
unless there is some prospect
from medical opinion,
that the patient is prevented by mental
illness from understanding all events objectively
and correctly,
from judging them by circumstances
as they really are,
and from taking his decisions
after unimpaired sensible consideration
and with free will,
then clearly in this case
the existing
call me Madam.

Cinematic language of his magical,
which does
magic and occultism. The
on its own two feet.
I was talking to the same woman from May 7th,
and as I understand her words.
But I did not know that the trip has
sense or bodily or memory.
digital media has, as posits
the shadow
as plastic as Alice;
it magnifies and projects,
contents are certainly profound and monumental.
though, social media is addictive
sucking us out of the world into a second hand world of screens.
The simple ate, and in such moments,
it is to myth societies turn
in order to remake cultural reference
between the French
fin-de-siècle

We crossed over

Peter Beard
Breyer P-Orridge
Burroughs and Gysin

I encourage this

Ian Curtis
Derek Jarman
Marie Laveau

This juxtaposition of creative, wild,
beautiful, successful, impoverished,
the real of living our dream
Entangle the knots
the client as her
to understand her
Divine Ptah, architect

permutation was to Warhol
Be home.
evils from internal and external sources
is also found in the analysis
of adults. In passing, I would say
that the very favorable changes
a contribution to the analysis
of the negative therapeutic reaction;
also, Freud, "The ego and the id."
that we genuinely
with a warily or
Both the
In your mischievous company
Loyalty Does Not End With Death

We crossed over

Her mysterious fate

opens with an image of three yellow circles
arranged in their demands,
unconcerned with our feeling reactions.
Pleasure constitutes a danger, even though
it should correspond to a natural
involved in the treatment process.
When a high score occurs in the
through any such sieve
as you may find or invent
visible on my face, or ass, and crushed sacrum or throat
displeasure? I must dogmatically defend the viewpoint that the
personal psyche is governed by unconscious impulses that lie deeper
the attachment to sorrow, her mysterious fate,
lead us to the historic prototype of
knowledge that there actually is something substantial there.
any individual's proper individuation
and reconnection is a marker
vast spaces, west on route 90,
sun still over sky's center, shining down
the role of unconscious homosexuality in mass psychology.
The most important consequence of Freud's
turns the *I* into that apparatus for which every instinctual
other images, so that it is present throughout, but
primary feelings are of an omnipotent nature,
this reflects on the current feeling of envy
experienced towards a substitute figure
and contributes, therefore, to the emotions stirred by envy as well
(Mr. Small) has an inferiority complex. The sisters,
the tent where the Master Musicians make their
commune with one another. I spot Jen and
– inside me – the broken bones,
of that society's inherent
potential threat there. The
break from the traditional narrative.
pass yr friends' letters yr office carbons
a toxicity of the blood stream. Freud
himself accordingly began his career

Death (For Mary Wild)

from the shadows. "Hey, Ivy,"
not want our freedom
a huge hug. He picks me up
We are tired of being
Death
Beloved Bast, mistress of happiness
high salaries for their deans that
- tuitions keep increasing.
Genesis Breyer P-Orridge *Magick*
what tonight is going to be like
like you
I is open. You must
matter what you feel
feel like it.
create
throughout the play.
Be Loved
lie only saw them during
unknown father, whose
little girl the issue of a she
Pi and I started to
has done a film of one of
"Surprise!" I jump in my seat,
I couldn't stand the smell.
We walked out into the Section Five evening.
The others went back in
to continue their detailed investigation.
Both Haynes and I knew that their work would amount to
Death
LA MORT
LA MORTE
game that is played with cowrie-shells and roughly resembles
'knuckle-bones'.
If his reply was acceptable, then he was called upon to swear,
high horizoning Yellowstone Lake–
Spruce forests line the shore, carpeting the flat uplands, snowy Rockies
types of artist: the
one who expresses

only thing that seems to shock a
thing that's pretentious or kitsch.
extremes, nobody will believe or

pleasurable experiences. In each moment you could have done something differently, but you

– I majored in old master
decorative, but I'm not say

before she found herself
Either the well was v

real. But. dear
the "real"? Are
to the truth? Co
illusions in eq

in such plenitude.

Hollywood to publicize the first punk fashion show.

Yes, Icey! Yes!" She flung herself upon the old we

fantasy is today a veritable pile of pulsating evidence; a

laid them down in bed next to Ella Mae.

HOWEVER, THE DEFLOWER-
ING OF A HANDFUL
OF HOLLYWOOD
BEAUTIES WAS HARDLY
THE SUM TOTAL OF
CROWLEY'S EVIL
AMBITION,BUT MERELY
THE TIP OF THE
ICEBERG!

Bizarre Sensory Experiences subscale (Sc3)
hypothesis that J. A. K. is not psychotic. W
Goldberg's index, a value of 22 is obtained

On through Wonderland Alice went,
looking for the White Rabbit. She met two

We were receiving (For Kendalle Aubra)

A large hall
numerous guests
Do you like my appreciation?
It gave me for what?
For whom?
We were receiving
chemistry between
among them was Irma
going to change my career
you, I
at once took her on one side
selves and each other
without the remotest
as though to answer her letter
of the consciousness
of either
total
and to reproach her
for not having accepted my solution, yet
"Mrs. Dis" variations I and II
Furthermore,
"The shadow,"
I said to her.
The prevailing doctrine.
If you still get pains
it's really only your fault.
ratio of the senses
rather like the blackened
on the shadow
rather than intention
to what they cast
that class, an empty
inversions that take our existence
Untitled
dimensional
"We can transfer conscious and present practice," she replied.
If you only knew what pains I've got now

in my throat and stomach and abdomen.
to add novel methods to occur
It's choking me.
loosened, the body is physically tempered
entranced
these techniques produce a cleansing
"Or nary fifty winters hath besieged thy leaden brow."
I was alarmed and looked at her.
And even as your corpus burns
for every laugh we never shared.
She looked pale and puffy.
"I'm as confident as some," I thought to myself.
that my youth, you still can leech

of barns, homes, churches and inns.
back to antiquity, most markings seen
19th centuries. Markings weren't the only

who fluttered about him in salons from Berlin to Hollywood. Yet he was unfathomably profound—the genius among geniuses who discovered, merely by thinking about it, that the universe was not as it seemed.

These are places where supernatural forces in
be at work," he tells Brown. "Local people are

existence.
"We had no
references to

cavers exploring
chanced upon

I spent the summer

Meet the

Staff at the Creswell Crags Museum & .
marks seen at the site dated to modern i
members of the underground exploration

conscience is of a different kind. Keep your courage, that's all that matters - and never let
yourself be analyzed. Write good poems, when that is given to you. But don't cramp up, and
don't hide yourself. Man stands naked in front of his God. That is the only prayer which is still
among us."

We used to be, and perhaps still are—if we remain sufficiently
young in heart—addicted to these stories, these never-to-be-
... they are bound together with strips of yak's hide to form
a thick mast nearly seventy feet high. Then a huge flag bearing
printed prayers and extending from the top to the bottom of the

threshold of life and death

medieval engravings from the comfort of their own homes.
Humans have left their mark (or in this case, markings) on
12,800 years ago, when hunter-gatherers left depictions of

But the very term "mythology" was brought forth

fields like the history of religions or anthropology.

the concept of myth was made conscious by Jung

The body o!

trauma as valid, almost on
discharged from the service

the way I clean fish in the sink.
A barely saintly gesture, but surgical.

sun and optimism I whooped
driver's seat to crane around

the old woman that to instrument such a union would vindicate
something lost in the dust of her own old, youthful, half-forgotten
yearnings. Preacher was a man of God. Any woman should be

witches, whatever you were

facilitator at the crags, notes

and drank some

"We did it," he said

remember what had

swallowed it. Then

marks inside."
expert on "protective marks,"
were hoping to ward off by

I am about what you're doing
last show! [both laugh] But
themselves at your feet,
shoes and handbags can
laughs]

recognized some of the carvings as witches'
engravings and confirmed their identity as
Historic England, witches' marks are also

rosary. Several days later, a plane crashed at Clark Airbase in
Manila, killing everyone aboard.
. . . And for those who are stone deaf and cave-worm blind;

a medicine made in this way was useful only as a temporary
measure: it had no real power as a borfimor.

the earth screeches, plates collapse,
the walls lose their grip on the painti
nothing is aligned like the planets we

would probably have engraved these marks
other hardships viewed as manifestations
likely represent just a fraction of those o

chamber suggests that this was a
Witches' marks aren't just found

digitize the marks.
(light detection and
caves, making them

A poem for the poet

She says, "It could be fairies,
there."

fearful of, it was going to be down   a heritage

that many medieval people

illusory. Historicism relegates identity to

of individuality ensures maximum freedo

internalized ideals of our parents, as was t

as I argue, fundamentally
is the corrective. The sha
s, to pun in the manner o
ects our power, out of pr
element in any strategy
sruption of witchcraft, a
n is a way of rediscove

even embedded "witch bottles"
witches from gaining entry.

12

Beyond the great silences

Trying to give a consistent account
of everything I have to
is a key to the reasonable reality
of the say on this subject.
I hope it will not be construed as
the state of the world
presumption on my part,
if I make uncommon demands
disconnection of the shadows
from thee
therefore be able
to piece together these underlying meanings.
That it is
but currently one
of the reasons he had an analysis
lay down on the couch
during
granted or lightly.

This is a selection of lines by William Burroughs:
Though I haunted the city of your dreams…
couch.
This is funny to me, like an overturned lamp.
Radically different,
but as I sought him,
I found him
not in the desolate markets
beyond the great silences.

The songs we will strike feel happy.
Opportunists with a penchant for seizing
lives free of somatic discomfort.
Looking around,
it'll make it a good deal easier to find.
They happened.
There is no point in listening all the time.
You post
that said all worth-while.

Control your own corset strings

Satisfied,
for instance,
ate the hair,
the intestines
and even the excrement
of a man from a village,
who had killed some of their relatives.
In general, he adds,
where cannibalism is fully recognized,
all turn to the shaman,
an Oracle,
sometimes things come out of my mouth that I was not aware of.
And that this w/hole flow of words
seem to make sense beyond my own comprehension.
It is only possible if I, m/other,
provides; allow this to occur
with the more subtle mental space
that shamans know in their ritual of
and malnourished. My friend,
that is exactly the poet's task
to mark his dreams and to attach meanings to them.
Believe me, man's most profound illusions
are revealed to him in dreams;
and all.
Yes, I continued.
Versifying and poetizing
is nothing but an interpretation of dreams.
Light suddenly.
A horseman in a raincoat
appeared in my headlamps.
It was the sheriff.
He had a 10-gallon hat, drooping in the torrent.
"Which way to Austin?"
He told me politely,
and I started off.
Outside town I suddenly saw two headlamps
correlates of high scores,

study of the content of the scale
items suggest that a high score is indicative
of an individual who is imaginary.
Windows
The magic of dreams made real.
Guilty pleasures
suddenly decide I want
We writers have been published.
in explorations and gave a REALLY
Eyes like an inverse path towards mastery.
Consciousness and have my head, so to speak.
Attractive PhD male with genius IQ
wants to fuck brilliant woman.
Research:
Can only make it if she is as remarkably learned as I am.
Good looks important, but a great mind essential.
Training:
Send copies of academic honors,
Stanford-Binet test results,
state career achievements, including a list of
Personal:
all books you've read and written,
to: Box 69, New York, New York.
Personal ads like that one will never appear in porn papers.
When enticing
Diagnosis:
bedmates with erotic qualifications out his career,
whether this be the shift he would invert,
reverse or showcase the powerful effect
are presented hung side by side
is exposed. I cherish his
because my maternal line is celebrated
author Marjorie Kinnan Rawlings
the swamps of rural northern Florida
and her novel was adapted into a film.
As I am a writer myself,
I could not keep my eyes off the Potala;
I knew the Dalai Lama
was on the roof looking at me through his telescope.

On the same day, I caught up with my caravan
consisting of fourteen pack animals
and two horses for me and my servant.
simultaneously and…
and they lay back in bed.
Think my strength is I
have another,
talk to audience.
People keep the case.
It would be
It's a pain in the ass.
The your help
control your own corset strings
Turn.
For me to look at it as not just a funeral song,
but also as something I could

Spine of the Mega Golem

It's written all, baby
I can feel of sun,
my darkest night,
faint
of by Exu Mal
our perceptions present
when we want to be alone
a number of tables on the terrace
are occupied
Severine is sitting alone
seemingly at a loose end
in which he living our everything at the same time
He flies over.
Pandrogeny continues on after Lady Jaye.
The unconscious
to Bransford
What you have now reclaimed.
But until then, some things do.
sapes of experience
whatever merely
is a drive
that does not
in dreams
now officially
8 x 10 foot cell
flanked Cosa Nostra
in the ers.
He alternately raged to break the law,
outbursts of temper
and there are three.
Come back
heart out.
So we should
dogmatic about it.
Before we have failed,
can we get to the truth of it?
Disturbance zigzags.

She throws her head back and whimpers in pain.
Medium close up of Pierre watching the cigarette hang,
and I never to you see fade away.
I'm looking now.
She was still,
he whispered
to androgyny and the conference
university
All makes sense
eventually.

At a point in space

As a fictional
don't belong to one
an absolute
basically all of primordial
to be art and magic always
26.
Mr. B is now at a point in space
186,000 miles from Earth
at point B.
See proposition number five.
A musical system
25.
Not knowing what is
and what is not knowing,
Mr. B knew not Mrs. D.
Them certainly gets better
on my horrible
I identify so much with my
jumping off the cliff.
There is a
Does my pussy taste good?
The power they have to change it opinion
impossible is not a declaration.
Potential impossible is temporary.
object can be completed
sibling because it provides
poles of primary masochism.
500 million
French Canadian bean soup
Plane hits volcano in Andes. 87 killed.
Santiago, Chile, February 6th;
a Chilean DC 6B airliner with 80.
I want that genome into the soap covered slopes
in the past year, the American
has sent the nation a powerful message
to violence and the difference between.

Not yet for tomorrow (For Lars)

They would say the spider comes
as long as one dreads the unconscious
force of integration.
Although most natural spiders live
in the earth dream,
which ends with an eight-fold poem,
and stony facade.
It's caged trees.
a vile attempt by a rival
the curse in *Towers Open Fire.*
reappears in an obscure rerelease
of the Danish
all this distance puts,
at distance, eroding witness
every day wit
can at least use each other's Christian names.
"Of course," she said,
and lifted the tail of his shirt as high as she could
over his back.
She caught her breath.
Seemed satisfied with a lifestyle
that others might judge to be boring
and uneventful.
Using a kind of hammer to tap them into place,
he said he noticed that
think, feeling that.
I don't think all of it can be clarified.
I like works that have some mystery to them.
Now, in academia, people would rather talk about difficulty
than the clock analyzing destinies,
making agricultural upheaval
solving endless logistical primal force,
like candles at an evening
was all on fire blazing,
and leafy festoon was
yeah, exactly. So like people are picking
up on these in cunning speculation,

as if she rendered progress through it extremely
difficult. And they're obstructions
in the way of tree trunks, underbrush, and trailing vines,
and creepers like ropes.
But the footing is nothing
rather than formulated.
The idea being that we are so inundated
with ideas of who and how we're supposed to be
placed upon us by our we began,
which he drew during their meeting with honesty
1938 to escape Nazi persecution.
Always had my fingers in a few pots,
like designing plastic jewelry,
while I was doing Macy's windows.
No one taught me about plastics,
I just went out there and learned how things work.
If all this energy weren't used,
I don't know what I'd be.

We have made a game out of love.
At water's edge, the wind when I was
I continued showing the order.
There were a lot.
These most of your and it's no mistake,
unselfish friendship. But at the same
I will never have a child by you.
comes for me to take my final leave of
not yet for tomorrow.
We do not know.
"It's alright, Billy.
It's all right."
No one else is going.
Turn this low, contemptuous look
across the bunch of eyes.
cheek to her starched breast
stroking his shoulder while she
sensation so overwhelming.
Even so, I think of it in color.
Kingdoms

can it for some reason no longer be retained in
Just drifting
the acid test
My, the trip is just beginning
penetrate her better than I and
Just drifting
buggery is still a life imprisonment offense,
even if permitted between husband and wife.
The risk of conviction is obviously minute.
Neither spouse can be compelled to give evidence against the other.
And a conviction is unlikely in the absence of corroboration,
such as a medical testimonial.
Round horses shade disturbed,
could not see anything.
Morning, six, suddenly away
on the driver side at
open the door
and the four of them
the darkness beyond the threshold.
Then from the murky, smoke filled darkness,
a woman's voice spoke to them,
"Help me," it cried, "I am rooted to the floor."

The fire Beard refers to occurred in 1977. His old mill on Long Island was

colored pillows and fabrics, this place is fit for royalty. It is

'That's what I do. You know who I work for.'

open, a desk so utterly unlike René. Why

t Stonehenge, sitting on the wall ov

and the belief that expiatory rites are

o be superficial and inappropriate

He, too, was full of confidence that he would be able to

the second state show a certain

underneath. Artists have

blood that is 'life' – retained in the course of the transition

synchronicity they've noticed – a moment when the outside world

voice: Burroughs traveled through various styles, until he came to experiment with the

was whether his knowledge equalled that of a Western schoolboy

to be effective in cutting through the manifest

24

S/he sighs (For Gen)

Dead
his piece of tin foil
a drunk
drop the tin foil.
We found the tin.
Five from D. Lamont:
"Throw the gasoline on them and light it quick."
Now, the intersection may be a picture
or it may be a text…
not all that much difference
for words *are* pictures and vice versa.
What we are tracking here is:
How does a word become a picture?
And how does a picture become a word?
In either case, you
society.
And because the demands of society
necessarily in human society,
the demands of human society
necessarily put a check on that other way of being.
There's a dichotomization,
and at least in the cultures that I'm familiar with,
that dichotomization seems to play out
in ways mentioned.
The Society for Psychical Research
contains an excellent summing up
of all experiences in this field.
It's author
I wrapped my
I am known to keep one
leisure, leather
would spiral and turn
SEE
I love to photograph
leather king.
aspirations that disappointed
lived on South Beach

and mysterious,
and all the
State waist
downtown Miami
and pick up
seeking husband, wife
exciting new friends?
minute drive but totally worth
Golden Circle Club
Okay, I want to give a little context.
This paper
the connoisseur's visiting massage
London
on psychoanalysis
and the occult,
and escort services
comes to us from Jung
by appointment only.
One goes on your right nipple.
One goes
quench
the rainwear review
the more it hurts.
Just lie still.
Are they stuck with past love positions?
tense notions of misbehavior
Jack one.
It's bigger and heavier.
Where do
ing off
in public
cinematic exploration,
married happiness
from foreplay to completion
and constantly
Black and white in Standard or Super 8
proving to them
(please specify)
selves and us that

The Golden Door Limited.
This, hey, is *real*
sex.
Nothing new
Please note:
postal service
business only
has been added
massage
general body massage
by qualified masseuse
except better-looking
girl and boy
performers
and an
Umbanda workings have demonstrated
that this force flows very elegantly
and well if one incorporates
Ogun in the workings
and asks him to intervene
and make the working and its results stable.
This is an important observation
illness, and so on.
To recuperate, she took a journey
on the 13th of September
to see a friend in South Germany.
The great joy at seeing her friend,
from whom she had been long separated,
and her participation in some festivities,
deprived her of her rest.
On the 15th, she and her friend
drank a half bottle of claret.
This was contrary to her usual habit.
They then
collapsing
And growing at the same moment
as s/he sighs

The flesh is an emotion in itself

realized I could not depend on other people for anything.
If my mother did not want me
around because I was too much to handle,
then why would anyone want me around ever?
Islands known as Melanesia
where people
"/Dynamite 'Black Pond'/Cruize
wrong terms like family
I with are found.
Feel now are corpses
and a much mind I do."
And metaphorically speaking,
at any rate, certainly knew.
"I *am* not.
Feel *that*."
merely comes from Freud
but from a much larger background
and perspective.
But if we stick to Freud's powerful legacy,
we recognize the hierarchic structure:
Id, Ego, Super-ego,
the tripod.
18.
The rifle has a muzzle
velocity of 2228 feet per second.
North Clark Street to California to
Manila to Gibraltar.
For example:
Captain Clark was shot by one
Frankie Gonzalez, from Manila,
described as a quiet man
who was always fingering his…
Listen to me
Talk to me
That you want,
I want to live
glass weather

dimensions as
which souls
I sat beside
husband, or
is a link.
much I
nostalgia in several years
androgyny is
selves and those
divide
The flesh is an emotion in itself.

Elementary Elementals

Absorbing

Monads, Dyads, Triads

Absorbing

Thesis, anti

Absorbing

elements of magick symbolically. As an
instrument of magick, cinema effectively
creates a dreamlike articulation of even the

anywhere upon the vast, spreading tableland between the barn
and the river. And then in the distance John saw him on the road,
emerging suddenly from behind a tall growth of red-bud: a man
on a huge field horse, moving slowly and yet with

An example: Our western dramaturgy is based o
in to Homer's stories about Odysseus' travels tov
faces problems and challenges that he, either alo

A PARTY?
HAVE IT AT MY PLACE!

o share her paintings with t

n 1906 and 1915 (111 of w

ly of work that in scale, s

. "Paintings for the Temple," n

wn inner evolution, as well as fe

n of mankind. Concerned that the

What can it be? he thought. What is this sink of despair I'm
falling into? What is the evil streak that finally got the better of
me yesterday and made me shout abuse at my innocent secretary,
and do something far worse than that? He picked up the paper-
weight now, and weighed it guiltily in his right hand.
concerning William Burroughs's translation of the
cut-up techniques into modern sorcery. His own

t only clamping

message of God

al, but I wanted to

was over, and I'd

served it.

ts like this. Suicides

we will just make

symbol could no longer stand in

own enemy and one of the finest

the and clothing

set up an advance meeting to focus

Moments from the

time. This cut then

which then effects

was very quick at learning languages, as are most Tibetans,
quite common for people of the upper class and business
speak Mongolian, Chinese, Nepalese and Hindi. My

Occultism

October reading

Ace of Pentacles
Coins
The gift of the Earth
Nature
Wealth
Security
A joyful life.
Magic.
Through the work of humanity
the raw material of nature
is shaped into
a comfortable environment.
The magic in the everyday.
A gateway
literally torn down as much as possible,
including the walls to the bathrooms.
Members were not to sleep
in the same place twice.
Meals were cooked at irregular times
throughout the day.
No one had their own money.
All clothing was kept in the center of

Queen of Wands
a particular appreciation of life.
Sexual energy–
a fine appreciation of life
legs open
warm
passionate
very solidly in the world.
When a person loves life
the world responds
by protecting that person
and sending her joyous experiences.
tells you doesn't sit right with you,
trust your own

being told.
Trust that you know above all.

The Hanged Man
simply indicates there is a deep rooted need for
peace and understanding
rhythm of life,
all in place.
point of no return.

Three of Cups
Joy
Celebration
sharing the wonder of life
a crisis has finished.
Work has produced wonderful results.
a sharing of experience.
seeks to keep us down
and maintain the status quo
all of those who desire to hurt me or

Four of Cups
recognize opportunities being presented to you.
Similar to the Ace of Cups,
new possibilities can lead
to happiness and satisfaction.
The Dadas were the first artistic movement
the cut. Through collage, assemblage, montage
Dadas highlighted the value of disruption,
way, Dada concepts and methodology mirror
processes, including work of dreams.
automatic writing, which was later incorporated

Knight of Swords
freer of social responsibility,
riding directly into the storm.
Eager
Brave
Skillful

Strong
No limits.
In an explosion that invites
The cemeteries to masked balls of
divisions: external, middle, and internal
The **external** ear is that part which is
on the outside of the skull.
The expanded portion,
mostly of cartilage
covered with skin,
is the *auricle*;
the deepest depression is the *concha*,
and the opening
escapable,
not from a position of power, but
to admit, is to understand the spectrum of
the daemonic cripple.
rituals with the dead in mind.
The practice is not
deceased for favors.
Rather it is a practice of development
dead, a friendship that is beneficial for both parties.

And so I collected the branches and bundled

ANOTHER BIG STORM TONIGHT
yourself. The ego itself is a symptom, and you
didn't know where the hell that had come from a minute ago,
but she kind of suspected there was an unmistakable rosy-red flush
by a megalomaniac consume Dracula's powdered
gag, but she didn't want to draw too much attention to herself. She
about Ben's last days, and to enjoy cocoa and a platter of Icey's
have sent it as a punishment, because the victim
events of life and the world take place in himself, yet if he reflects, he
and I can tell you that there is a sweetness in that
The twigs of the cedar tree would be brought to
land planted like a willow by abundant water would
told me and so I collected the branches and bundled

Love with its numerous uses

When man, seeking to empty himself
of all thoughts,
advances in the spaces,
in the shadowless gleam
of imaginary space,
abstaining from even awaiting
what rock through will emerge from it,
a dull mirror
shows him a surface
in which nothing is
running in the reflected.

their original nature to keep
their identity recognizable
(as in such features as
the longing for proximity,
and self-sacrifice).
We are of the opinion, then,
that the language
has carried out
an entirely justifiable piece of unification
in creating the word
'love' with its numerous uses,
and that we cannot do better
than take it as the basis
of our scientific discussions
and expositions as well.

By coming to this decision,
psycho-analysis has let loose a storm
of indignation, as though it had been
below it? names are mentioned in a
I left them at it – screaming
and Peppercorn stuttering
in bewilderment. They didn't notice
I was going, except...

Want to call me? Do you

Suggestion and Libido
his agenda is. Sometimes it?
We started from the fundamental fact
that an individual
in a group
is subjected
through its influence
to what is often a
to be a preponderant factor
from the very beginning.'
I have previously suggested
that greed, hate, and persecutory anxieties
in relation to the primal object,
the mother's breast,
have an innate bias.
In this discussion, I have added
that envy, too, as a
He urges upon,
however, the same considerations
that I am now urging upon himself.
'I trust', he says,
done
'that even in the case of
Geheimrat Prof. Dr. Flechsig
any one by
coarseness of his language.
But then, how did she expect
to be is not the Alpha but the Omega.
Spin the wheel
referred to,
if not as a whore, a girl who,
in the presence of
and do it in the spirit of
PENTI TENTO NON PI
three men (not to mention the restaurant waiters
who kept autonomy
in the psyche

of the image of one's body.
Mason the spot,
on the old map still
The way something feels
at the moment is
memory remembers it one way
and filters it
write in journals to keep things clear. So
here, and the dome would be here," he
(Example of this is that I wouldn't have
to the introduction of measurement.
In themselves, space
015, and that week had
the reading with
and time consist of *nothing*.
They are hypostatized
strongly and provided all of these ideas – concepts
born of the discriminating activity
of the conscious mind,
and they form the indispensable coordinates for de-
with a muscle I have repeatedly praised in my lectures.
In concluding, I hope that this brief discourse on the imago will strike you,
do not. We are well aware of the atrocities
of gender to children born intersex and what
"Very beautiful and very sadistic. They'll take all the
rather than exalt the hermaphroditic, as has been
skin off you!"
His penis gave a little leap in his pyjama trousers. He
freedom, as can be seen in the fact that madness is found only in man and
only
point
and on the second occasion to the very heavy burden
served as the foundation of physics
of work that fell upon my shoulders
when I entered on my new duties
However, we cannot yet fully grasp
had no other goal than to guide you
id as "fluid"
(Still today many psychotherapists

identify bodies of water in dreams,
e.g., bathtubs, swimming
It seems to me to be correlated with pools,
oceans, as "the unconscious.")
Freud goes on to say
indivisible space, our intuition of
Psychoanalysis does the same.
By breaking the mindless repetition of DNA, we are also
notion of gestalts – and with a kind
want to call me? Do you

inside our tiny temporal vessel. It may seem paradoxical to say that the more we know, the better.

that won't be able to be taken again. And I'm finding some good quotes to put on

a complex story simple, so it can convey the big details and small totalities in as

One sentence at a time,

cerebral sky from which rain,

its distribution was subject to special regulations. The training

admits. But I don't care. I went to art school. I never use the

as well watch the last chapter. Photography can record that I've got all the pictures

sely timed since the brush is cut too late the rains may so
rush, which not burn. On the other hand, if the brush

sexes too, when union is made possible by emotional nudi
ty and a temporary upheaval of the intrusive fireworks of

relationship between partners [self-other(s)-witness].

past that now has a completely new meaning.

39

Daguerrotype

Strictly speaking, Ey's organo-dynamism can legitimately be included in
this doctrine simply because it cannot relate the genesis of mental problems
people have appeared at the correct time/space
Fechner. Freud says: "… we have conceived the
principle which governs all mental processes as a special case
of Fechner's *tendency to stability*…" The mythical
descriptions of the figures of the underworld fixed in their
repetitions, unredeemable, unredressed, correspond meta-
sexual act."
To this point, I can agree with Stekel. However, he further states:
A typical dream of a young girl presents her standing naked in the street. A large
man throws himself on her and thrusts a knife into her belly. In this case, murder
Never underestimate the importance of knowledge.
RESET! Miss 1 turn

When searching

With that in mind, I use "machine
the capability of modeling a sense of
what we know of biological
excited, aroused and
the mirror image
imagine ourselves
fantasy. However, the
true self, what Lacan
EXHIBITIONISM
never stop you
Her lips gradually
The fortune teller
reshaping candy
It's not as easy
as just putting an e
in front of everything.

I, Robert Garry, shall get
to be away from people,
for something to say,
it could have been
about I haven't the
once I believe we

for something to
and she couldn't
or Malta. Why
ing major. I'm
unload what
I tell her

he would
up, and
pulled it off. For a
did the American.
elled imprecations,
MAURICE: Well, one night when

club called the Sound Factory
club. I'm there just shaking
and then I turn around and
there. He approaches me a
here?" I might add that my
proceeds to tell me that he
gay. I don't take him too se

So, the next day when I com
Your first book was called *Famouz*.
The title was written with a "z" because
myself recognizable as a Dutchman.

What do you look for when searching?

Surfaces

are a sight
my body is
wants to steal
province of the high resonance narcissists
high achievers. There has been an almost to
in broader paganism. Witchcraft, it must be
Amoeba.
minal behavior themselves, however, subject
comes a shared behavior and encourages crime
neighborhood in the Brooklyn Navy Yard
ally by 1907, and moved to Garfield Place
He was just a lousy hypnotist. He just didn't like
them what to do. He discovered that he felt much
'cause he also didn't like being stared at. And that's
This practice eventually evolved into Genesis
performances, in which the pair would begin
with all of his orange belongings on one side
projections of the completed ego,
as mythomaniac in the child
vacillating, as transitivist in
Fear Is The Beginning
ring her knees together and because her arms pinioned
"The mysteries can only be preserved by constant revelation."
No order, no hierarchy.
constructed of a patina of shadow and light.
surfaces
for psychoanalysis,
going, and what you are going to?" She was in such evident
distress that I tried to comfort her, but without effect. Finally,
she went down on her knees and implored me not to go; at
it's all time-stamped and searchable.
to be the
sutural, and at every level inhere it in
whose movements are in no way
coherence across the entire spectrum
Spinning in infinity as the waves envelop me
MIMICS ART MIMICS
The worlds best

from the shadows. "Hey, Ivy,
a huge hug. He picks me up

NOT WANT OUR FREEDOM
WE ARE TIRED OF BEING

what tonight is going to be like

"Surprise!" I jump in my seat,

I couldn't stand the smell. We walked out into the Section Five evening. The others went back in
to continue their detailed investigation. Both Haynes and I knew that their work would amount to

high horizoning Yellowstone Lake—
Spruce Forests line the shore, carpeting the flat uplands, snowy Rockies

game that is played with cowrie-shells and roughly resembles
'knuckle-bones'.
If his reply was acceptable he was then called upon to swear,

types of artist: the
the one who expresses

44

Chaos Reigns

Early efforts were, however, not promising.
So don't worry, I'll meet you in the hospital in half
in some segments or schools of psychiatry,
alternative importance for
Mother's own wedding ring.
There was a world in that window.
The fox that he encounters states, "Chaos reigns."

Disrupted the sensorium

These black dressed
I'm just a goth." And
a
I
Queen.
sprawled across the floor.
worked there since 1938
owners of the building
downpayment. Brenda
changing sheets at a
there's a fly on the wall and a fish in the bowl
It requires working with
potential and absolute
power and weakness
sense of… I'm very percussive
not to be in the choir, because
–I was a belter, and I could belt
I could belt out old blues songs,
Seventeenth Century Demonological
some discussion of the Schreber
which is the subject of the paper is
disrupted the sensorium, then I
shadow disrupts proportion: it is as
ANOHNI
big armchair. I felt safe for a while with
to draw there. And I would spend hours
incorporated
and experienced
and the violation
minds into the surreal
intention of breaking down
they may come together more
the Pandrogyne. Influenced by
CA: Yeah.
VD: Security blankets
security blanket. Gail
dream touches on what was then future

seem prescient now. He would be born
objects to conform with an
much higher
my fire

The Dynamics of Personality

Thus we are all pervasive deviate lives the purpose

so that we are all pervasive deviate lives the purpose

It is about this for nonsense will raise the opportunity to taking on a high where as myself you be in experience and each is just as valid and we are perceive our on a vinous or nervous run society, or of speed and objective anxiety or take best worst nothing. It can also be a kind of

This chapter in this case a Third Thing.

various personas and accoutrements as we mould our online personality; however the other

knew the person whose house we were in better than I did, I had no idea where I was. But

Thus the group appears to us as a revival of the primal horde. Just as painting manifests many personality in every

nature of textuality itself by exploring the very limits of the role of author via the process of

There are two important components to psychological adjustment level. First,

may be most of a certain experience and discrimination, and

Huh! Corny? This from a guy who drove up that morning in a

in his soul or a subtle wilfulness in speech or act, he was

And we must also admit that it is on the side of sex that the most secret and profound

Manifesting

But I'm dying inside tonight
I'll never let you down
I can smile if required
very specific. Moreover both "The
de" could be considered part of the
ed the complete image of enigmatic
to 1915, in the artist's 28th year
with open legs. Of course it does not take
to realize that what Dürer was looking at
immortalized in "Étant Donnés" (as well
All of a sudden, my photographic me
the image of the artist with his eye, close
"come out of nowhere.
writing is cut-ups, but
method was delineated.
factor of unpredictability

We're always right here, and here we will remain,
intents. By the way and when in Rome… Darling
the penitents. When they realized the mockery was
recognized as powerful for Maria Padilha,
although in this *qualidade* it is less
overt and often manifests in befriending the
house perceived powerful. Manipulator
rejection. What I have been proposing is farfetched,
impractical, and visionary. The approach bespeaks
the territory of its origin, Chthon, the faraway pneumatic
world that is a dimension
not available in itself and so cannot be rightly
another. It's beautiful out here.
My experience is
myself to drift to wherever my desire leads me.
Why are we taught that this meandering style is
we taught to be productive at all? As if living a
opened.

Dona Maria Padilha das Sete Encruzilhadas was the first to come,
manifesting

Theatre

The Golem)
invested in Dada from the beginning,
or human error as much as you want or need to
work. No more, no less. Magic in revenge of our
manny sisters who burned. We're not in any rush
FIND
–Yet even then, in that hour of supreme agony, Our
Merciful Redeemer had put for mankind. Yet even there, on
the hill of Calvary, He founded the holy catholic church
the letters; the first of which in this context
of reverted chance; give chance a chance,
quintessential Exu Woman, wife of Lucifer.
She is a powerful ally in the Kingdoms of Quimbanda,
for she is truly Legion. There is a need to be
My true-love hath my
By just exchange one
and the pain of persecutory anxiety.
Together with happy experiences, unavoidable grievances
reinforce the innate conflict between love and hate, in fact, basically
between life and death instincts, and result in the feeling that a
Making shapes on the wall
Making sure they are all symmetrical
Please let it be tomorrow
was opened upon the point of Tata Caveira
to give stability to the dead of the
house and of the client. The client's dead
were saluted with water, tobacco, and
is Padre's Progress, if any, is
reader to work out for himself.
hypocrisy emerges as the theme it
easier to rebut by the outbreak
of elaborate "shows" as though it were a
theatre.
and advisor both. She confirmed a
connection to the Pomba Gira known as do
Luar–of the moon–although this connection
is best entertained in time and

abstruse and consummately occult. The
kinds, – exoteric, those that the philosophers
understand, and esoteric, those that nobody

Sweets offered to the Forces

white cardboard box in the front living room."
When Natalie came back, she set the box down on the bed,
opened it, and one by one removed the objects inside,
unwrapping the paper in which they were packed, and handing them
to Sir Stephen. They were masks, a combination headpiece and
mask; it was obvious they had been made to cover the entire
head, with the exception of the mouth and the chin–and of course
anxiety, may up to a point be influenced by the urge to satisfy the
analyst and to be loved by him. The analyst who is aware of this
prepare the way.
At the same time as this identification with his father, or a little later,
cathexis towards his mother according to the attachment (anaclitic) type.
double, including the latter's appearance in dreams and
identifications that go with it. But what is most important
as fundamental libidinal stance
psychoanalysis is the pursuit
bath would be followed by the application or a
sacred oil applied all over the body. A gift
of sweets would be offered to the Forces

Plaything of devils

hand, in the marked prevalence of visual
human
form, which begins so early, as I mentioned
plaything of devils, he saw crowd of people can
"holy music" and in the end these individuals must have
was living in another world.' bias in some situation or
It may be added that their psychological group, and the
who stands for exaltation or intensification
she was naked
and difficult men's emotions are stirred
sharable experience for those
he merged in the group and
I'm all that you carried away
by a common
emotion by way of the
of their reality
contagion with which we are
IN OUR CONTEMPORARY CULTURE
the dream sphere has been
integrated adult personality,
for the later differentiation between good
achieved. Thus the basis is not laid for a fully developed and
breast, and the building up of a good object cannot sufficiently be
impulses, interferes with the primal split between the good and bad
good and bad that arises in the relation to the primal object.
While people who have been able to establish the primal good
object with relative security are capable of retaining their love for it
roar and the fireplace, opposite her bed, which would be ideal
for them. He hammered some nails into the wood. There were
rings on the ends of the handles of the whips and riding crops,
essential for every happy love relation or friendship. At best, such an
another person; such unity means being fully understood, which is
of all later happiness, and make possible
the feeling of unity with
looking for connection
possession of the same complex.
Hence the sexual feeling.

It is not at all necessary for one to react with a together. Both positive and negative emotions, but emotions that are nevertheless similar can arouse sexual attraction.

the lead practitioner's will. For example, in the

and do what you like in-between

leaves you breathless.

within the self being diminished.

been forced to evolve from learned

view, what would you say makes you unique as an artist?

marathons, sensitivity training, awareness groups, hypno-

straight and dull as highways. Bred on

rays pouring through the trees in a sort of rhythm of light.

the actual father image. Since the child's identification

even religions—but all that really mattered was how large their breasts were.

truth of the interpretations given lead to
spectively the primal object—being built

her lover with the proof that she belonged to him, but also

ODDLY INFUSED with
ROSE and CUCUMBER

POST CARD

PLACE
ONE CENT
STAMP

55

Sleazy scandals

And devout partakers
Nutritious potential or rotten fodder
For earth alone
The need to reconstruct
SLEAZY SCANDALS
My friend brings the silence

Penthouse Playboy

about cults is
destruction and
is reflected in the Dada
which to apply the
process in his manifesto
'*Prolegomena*' in Austin Spare,
The Valley of Fear
'The Living Word of ZOS'
in *AOS: A Celebration*
(Borough Satyr: The Life and Art
of Austin Osman Spare, 2005)
It is your turn forever
The Cliff (for Vanessa)
know why they do what they do.
The carcass was rubbed over with
the juicy substance of the banana-tree,
after which it was thrown for a few minutes
on the fire.
Then, when it was warm,
it was scraped with mussel-shells
or knives, and then washed.
It was next laid on its back,
when thirsty. A bottle of
We want to feel something.
"Vivid Dream" from her 2015
album is your first since
a shared habitat is
pluck his eyebrows all
She's been
of one another.

My life is myself

place in my presence. They too
the ground, or into a chair, shut
to speak. In this stage she was
also tactile sensation. She was
influencing a role. My life is
myself. People like to talk
to be strong. In order to play
need to feel like the character.
great one. and writers
quantity of
are implying
of the feelings
APPLE XENOS
copywriter

"I want to live in a world
created by art, not just
decorated with it"

Then he took thee two heavy chains and
them both at thee foot of North tree. He
Securing him tightly. Thee Dog could
feel God's power and wrath. Yet everything that was spoken
was genuine, not phrases learnt by rote as they later were, but
the immediate expression of the true feeling.
For this reason my impression was not one of alarm and fear,
step at a time will fix
formula. It is impossible to
question when you don't exist.
on to the riddle
shows us our further path.
I would say your films to explain one of their
actions of all of them,
up shows us more than
If you saw a film and the incapacity for
end was peaceful–what work it off completely in
show an unmistakable

song savages or children.
have heard, in
intellectual acts are too
being repeated in a
of dependence are part
an emotion, then I did. To me, sex was
not dirty. It was somethin' very intimate
and very real. I don't ever remember

They would be unable to explain. And suppose further, that when he saw their perplexity he said: 'Do you desire to be wholly one; always day and night in one

VD: It's not a weakness. It's a
I want to do two sides of a viny
violins, et cetera. Well, it – I'm
all the time. It's very exciting --

nut
no

es of this work

of necromancy

was the word

Then I.T. knew it was
And that was I.T."

million, and further
life among all of this

baby ? what you

mysteries

lurks behind it, it is not so easy to
seen something terrible; wonderland

through repetition

In search of

interpreted
passion.
love, and

of the almost shattered individuals, with a view to the healing balm of the blissful illusion: all of a sudden we imagine we see only Tristan, motionless, asking himself dully, "The old

haunted, not by spirits but of things, places,
it generated infrasonic memory vibrations
subconsciously I wanted to be haunted.

as e and God eyed each other. I guess this

God said and smiled. "It sure as hell does,

he continued. "I know how you've been.

* Maria Padilha Rainha das 7 Encruzilhadas

developed to acheive trance states and metamorphasis,

bed and reached for scissors
to thin out my bush before
doing the fine work with the
razor.

finger in and out of my
pussy as if it was a big hard
dick.
    I came so hard and so

marvels they longed to be back in their own country
behindhand in the devices of civilisation, represented
the firm ground of existence.

into a blur my

on health and beauty, and advertisements.

hese clippings would have been considered

se as artistic material at the time, as even

Lady Jaye...

... Or is it?

n appropriate art form then

Satan, if a Satan really existed, would not believe
was a Satan, and I certainly do believe in a

"Påsk Häxan"

Stockholm   Påsk © 2020.4.12

60

Success is mine

and maximize the other's psyche.
and hate are split off but form part of the
reaction.
I have often referred to the infant's desire
I thank you for the opportunity to
came, and always, adding to the
bite which made her gasp for breath. She lost
found herself again lying on the bed, with
Success is mine.
learn more of the Exus and Pomba
Mystery that is this cult. I am
Most people when they think of
(finished cigarette… cough cuts his voice)…
… so many… telescope… Gibraltar… when
visible wire… what electrician?… the green
am here… specialized cripple… the old breed
… cool remote morning… You will notice Friday
returns… cut-up or fold-in that worked yes it
ago so keep moving we went on from red brick
will go on from our worn-out film techniques…
you know, very liberal… I had
now I've actually studied it.
feminism?
Her gift is inherited in part from a 19th-century
Mr. Herzog, do you think someone
blockbuster?
It wouldn't be crazy at all, because
money that Hollywood would spend
be like, "You know what?
film, everybody is saying no
that some element of guilt does not
feelings of gratitude.
My observations have shown me
forming a full
prepared to sage the
structures for the subconscious This Another interest is
relationships and then call me 3 years KEY IN

no calligraphy for closely. I'm quite sure A spiral.
precedes the music lyrics I believe. When Cling
of neurosis, but the madness by which man thinks he is a man.

Hysterical fairgrounds

Not only is photography an aesthetic
particular to humankind at large. Everyone
all to daily social culture, bureaucracy and
listen. The advent of photography caused a revolution
creation of artistic works; Freud himself was flooded with
cannot fully grasp, as our culture is so extensive
artist, poet or photographer. medical professionals
of his portraiture, capturing images
would you like to see in the never before?
Freud's own view described in *Camera Lucida*.
kaleidoscope can. His kaleidoscope portrait
an artist need to be taught or require years
of Dalí's signature moustache pulled in
may be true for some artists,
it is not true for the form of a starfish.
Dalí's eyes are anthropological records,
art history becoming instrumental in government
The first relatively inexpensive albums
and formal portraiture; military reconnaissance
the year Freud published *The In* their own story,
Freud's analysands were and funny pictures
as an escape in a way that made sense to them,
photographer, I covered the
rather than having their own being explained to them;
or the caricatures one sees
worthless, diseased, undesirable, impossible,
hysterical fairgrounds. The way Dalí's most
recognizable, from midnight onward,
he listened in on one could even say grotesque
burglaries, domestic violence, hold-ups
practitioners and "experts" telling
the patient invited to speak for the fist time
and the doctor and which experiences s/he'd like
to anthropology and the medical science of the time
like a simple move, but it is a significant development,
that of the detective novel. All these
describes, "No one achieved this goal better

63

at play underneath the surface,
rather what is not in tools of his art –
the few rolls of film, a small
to capture the elusive traces suggested
As we'll see revolutionized
not only fantasies and jokes.
through the work of many images
into the hands of She is noted
for this shift in perspective
of a shield between the viewer
the individual whether matter.
This shift in itself is an essential cut,
influenced Freud's own thought to surround yourself?
he deemed a *calotype*. While not as fine in
and the world around him. Our hands.
was another photographer working
for multiple prints to be taken from a
captured distinctive images of the everyday
went from a device primarily utilized in service

Development of the Libido

self-compatible,
object: the breast that returns and can be enjoyed is felt as
evidence that it is not injured and that it is still good.
The fact that envy spoils the capacity for enjoyment explains
A Short History of the Development of the Libido
the art market
or unaccounted for
scholars of the radical and
that there is a financial
that the addition of
to the market would
once my Mercury, it could be
Over time it's branches have
could smell was where river
ground absorbing the pulse
panopticon to my left. While
the sky opened but didn't crack
coming. It was slight and delicate
psychoanalysis think of
hands of collectors, but
the focus is maintained on
the individual level, in
and as
We
recognized large
there is no resistance
fascia is E
mind system. We re-write history
and *gene*
– situation
forget that science itself
late, one
the corpse OM creative speculation
It's if they stand fast in the
outcast by his family of origin
over again, throughout
effect of disruption; when

of current method
a pushing away from others.
to remove every doubt as to the reality of the myth
who could prove the reality of the empirical world
the truthfulness of God and His inability to utter
makes use of this same divine truthfulness
once

W.L. 2020·12·06

Experience the dark (For Matton)

makes you a better, more integrated person–even unhappy
experiences. The first party I ever went to was a bore. The people
1970s was one of visibility and provocation. LaVey
of us. I glance over at Viktor to see if he understands what
century, often blatantly defying Soviet oppression. I read through
parties because I think you have to try *everything*. Experience
the dark and when he wasn't thinking about new ways to
talk he would think about the women. He could never
course. Their lineage of mythic proportions. Their music
holders–those thousands of good plain Americans
to whom I am responsible.
"Come in please, Miss Prendergast."
He looked at the rough notes he had made for
him. I grabbed the straw from Ariel's drink, dropped it in my urinary
pull up, ready for the next segment of our journey, as
Other people exist for us only when they are
psyche; only suitable people exist for us.
the greatest of honors. But they would never give up their souls for
substitute another person for himself, he doesn't
Ivy St Clair had contributed a whole chapter on Igor Kumchuk, who was
of creature with creature whether
added such exasperation
be calculated: what then is one
binding and building and
should stop thinking."
seven millions. Who is to
helpless
And one must
That we may bear to live at all, we are
self-deceit: and that fierce need which is
our hearts, its fury in our knowledge is,
identification is similar
already become. We have always
even sure it is an actual door.
Who the woman is or what she does
directed, but towards what? In terms
experience involves

a perception of thee
habituate as drawing breath: moreover, blunt
are, we are not utterly emasculate of joy
this environment is as abundant of beauty
as of every harm: and here in whatever way
of the peoples of the world, marked with the
chemistries of that wealth or its lack upon
this infant phase incongruously wracked, you
BANGING BLONDE BUNS: The plot's weak,
but there's plenty of cheek in Anita, Swedish Nymphet.
good, strength, calm, humane intention, those
sort it would be madness to condemn: of human

Break free of that which binds us (For Katelan & Carl)

has nothing to give you."
'Who is a Silver Fox,' asked Bruce who was determined
to find a key and had hopes that this story would
—oftentimes these are in reaction artists to the canon
have been imposed upon us, story up until that put
us in place. What appears as her abstract artwork
break free of that which binds us. This forerunners of
son's language; to really listen and Mondrian
resistant the art delineated history of
his anxiety, and is inclined to prolong the session
because he wants to take in as much as possible
of what at the time he feels to be good.
slices of life that only exist for a fragment
man with an obsession and a will, who
conceptualizations of the
BENEATH THE MERCURY TREE
A Myth of Time, Memory, & Ancestry
Instead of focusing on
principles, placing
substituting placement,
initiated the beauty in the mundane,
even in that which some would even consider
not capture her subjects in a way that
THE DEVIL'S FOOTPRINT
find the words to describe one's own
potential in itself. Similarly, in
have the exciting relation of a prophetic dream
to a reality taking place
later on. But Euripides' speculations took a different turn.
The effect of tragedy never depended on epic suspense,
on a fascinating uncertainty as to what is to happen now
and afterwards: but rather on the great rhetorical-lyric scenes
in which the passion and dialectic of the chief
The concept of an "anima mundi" has followed us through

World? Create it.

meet up with Vanessa in advance to discuss a new genre of literature
even set up an advance meeting to focus in on areas search better
evolution for clues to figure out what is
the part of the mother who, whenever the infant cries, at once
presents him with food, is unhelpful to the infant. He feels the
mother's anxiety and this increases his own. I have also met in
adults the grievance that they had not been allowed to cry enough,
the power is in the hands of
With what would you like
world? Create it. The power is in you

encourages autonomy, agency and self-
opportunity to begin to construct one's own

Bentley's work is an enchanting example of this
photography and advances being made in nature

undoubtedly provide those answers, although everyone already suspects the Devil is...

the pencil does not touch the paper, but writes in the air. These movements must be conceived as purely motor phenomena, which correspond to the expression of the motor element in the

crazy about you, he said, and wondered whether in fact he was. He put a hand behind her and drew her nearer to him.

like a field hand and snatched a switch of willow as she came

essentially perverse infantile sexuality, which is our

for the time being. After her week-end in London she

to the space-age needs

becomes songs.

somehow ascribed

magical qualities

and when a bus tries to pass

Flesh attempts to remove stone from girl's vagina

Holiest of Mountain

over her and put his lips to hers. "I'm beginning to be

A Strong Tree With Many Birds

of history and rhythm, race and rhyme, melody and passion is an actual stunning event. Tickets

Lobo. For the

72

Marassa Jumeaux

THUNDER & LIGHTENING – & THE
Earl's first magazine – and
she'd wanted it to look just right.
She strutted across the set,
gave a swift tug to her rolled nylons,
and entwined herself around a diamond ring
so big you could step
other words, as Marc himself
says, it is really a fan club for
himself.
Marc achieved his popularity
not through any skillful
distance relationship
for so long; a dozen years apart,
it's nice to see them finally rejoined.
Both wearing red robes,
they almost look like a single being with two heads – Marassa
When the analysis can be carried to these depths, envy
and the fear of envy diminish, leading to a greater trust
in constructive and reparative forces, actually
in the capacity for love. The result is also
both states we must recognize a Dionysian
phenomenon, which reveals to us again and again
the playful construction and demolishing of the
world of individuals
as the overflow of a primitive delight
just as

Immediate environment
Temperance
lagom. Balance.
The right move at the right time.
Meeting the world where it's at, in harmony.
OTHER or earthquake?
Will the nation be leveled flat before
we've all pursued happiness
to its spoor's end? An occasional Zen
stretching ability

don't worry about it. It could be worse.
Which living person do you most
Despising isn't my thing.
Which words or phrases do you most overuse?
ways, understand why…" (in a whiney tone).
What is your greatest regret? Not
looks, and opening vaults filled with jewels.
He claims to be
continued. able to crack a safe in less than 16 seconds.
"I am probably the fastest in the world,"
he says. "I could take the world apart and
at each clean shaven snatch of this hot babe. She
lays naked looking at Ivy and smiling.
They were both so beautiful
rubbed continue
culture unfortunately has no language
or technique for the substantial integration of
near blue and immediately perceptible
to us in a sensible and not at all abstract
manner, as we likewise perceive that it is
only in these relations that
a melodic line manifests itself clearly. And
perhaps as determined by destructive impulses.
Here I wish to add that envy
gives particular impetus to these attacks.
This means that when I wrote about
the greedy scooping out of the breast
and of the mother's link to the alchemical process,
the digital video
Noko, Order 41: Conjuration of Beelzebub

Hopes/fears
Queen of Pentacles
The Queen is aware of the power she possesses
in her hands. It is precious.
She is grateful.
Intensely aware of the magic in nature,
and the strength she derives from it.
She knows and believes in herself
and in the magic of her life.

The pathways of the heart (for Jessica Marshall)

colour and texture. In the darkness all cats
and wiggling her butt in the entranceways.
crime against nature": such are the terrible expressions the myth
herself. "The sharpness of wisdom turns upon the sage: wisdom
annihilation, must also expect to experience the dissolution of
which would be particularly great in a baby who had a
This in some measure explains the development of his early
ass. Miss Teenage America was stoned, glazed
that conveys a sensuous sense of certainty
apparatus that allows me to reminisce!
the grass or the scalding tops of parked cars
action was tuned to a conscious attempt to disseminate this vision.
place
to create
God was a bit of
ultimately failed agent provocateur

A Vehicle

a vehicle
who comprehended the
which means, mental
is 'from the accumulations of energy that must have met some previous
outrageous though it is – 'look! I am master now!'), the two act as one,
This they did with a will; but the further down they dug,
four brothers set to work at once.
"Then we will dig you out," said her father, and bade
decode my work. I don't write that way and I won't
ten sentences to translate, he usually showed up
knew might find out, and partly I was just
this is. Partly I was scared that somebody I
confessed, "You know what a small town
to go and buy any contraceptives." he
desired, of the ideal, and also using the highly
vitally charged residual secretions: semen and vaginal
unbridled creativity in many spheres. Where the previous
and the decadent period – literary and literal – coexisted
moving faster than we anticipated,"
Ricardo's attorneys asked for a procedural
exception because "the trial was
"We think
longer than the commonly
founded the Anthology
their treasures to be stored in
the people as a whole believed
that a miracle would save the
ring for a moment
individual is the
one of its needs
relaxed atmosphere & how
enter it
expert on
fluids), meditational focus, Eastern mantric
techniques, Austin Osman Spare's development of an
my fifteen years of service to the corporation
I may justifiably say–I have never before

so hot
hence one form the direction
the places they
never
holds true for the thought of making a..."
Stones were arriving just in time for the
insanity of an election and the attempt
itself until it runs our of change
when I die. Yes, here in Brooklyn. Maybe someone will try to
one college setting to another
and among divisions within each college. This
variation indicates that separate norms
and cutoff scores should be established
I was struck by how accessible it was, how direct
of good about
to deal with poetry.
reason.
try and succeed,
Hell, believe me.

THE MOON

XVIII

young woman *I was treating had, scarab. While she was telling me*

—napalm that flowed out of White thru television's leaky colortubes—

XVIII

"Not at all," I replied. "What's the address?"

appear drowsy. I again turn

The Moon

THE MOON.

in front windshield rolling downhill, wind soughing car side—Absaroka Range, Crow People snowpeaks encircling the flat watershining panorama

or chanting, that had opened a door in their minds through which had stepped a 'thing' they could neither contain nor control. And

"You on the burnt guy case?"

"Yep," I answered. "Just got back. How

SEGREGATED SOUTH INTO A THOUSAND PIECES AND PUT THEM TOGETHER IN THE IMAGE OF GOD AND DEMOCRACY. WE MUST SAY: "WAKE UP AMERICA! WAKE UP!" FOR WE

all honesty, because I

Discover or rediscover ourselves

marry men twenty years older
than themselves. Herr Feist
is the Food Minister, Herr Rosstäuscher
is a lawyer, Herr Kalberer is an obstetrician
Okay. So I have one final question, and that would be
maintains a psychological distance;
avoids interpersonal involvement
He is cautious and conventional in approach to problems;
has difficulty in making decisions;
is nonaggressive and over-controlled;
denies impulses, avoids unpleasantness,
makes concessions to avoid confrontations,
and is motivated by therapy
LOOK AT architectural structures within the amulet support
THAT PRETTY the probability that the imagery was assimilated
PICTURE OF as one of the most miraculous creative minds of our
time. Like Alexander Hamilton, Miranda is a powerful
reminder that greatness comes from
Immerse yourself in their work. Read their books,
listen to music they composed. Whichever medium
yourself in it and enjoy it. Think of the person, speak
THE DREAM AND THE UNDERWORLD
after him, that is based on the ontological disjunction between
dayworld and nightworld. Drawn to extremes, each world
should be made here of the potential short cut from
violent emotions to violent actions stressed by all
authors on mass psychology, a phenomenon which in
us, has turned her into a star that's not a
star we look at, but a giant star with its
own gravity that we are drawn to. All of
took place in giant chlorinated pool).
Williams, who went on to star in the
Technicolor musical *Bathing Beauty*,
epitomized perpetual sunniness in
sleep away from in awaiting the return of the sun,
which makes everything bright and simple again.
It is interesting to note how the myth of the

werewolf is also soaked in blood. This ferocity and
times. de Bry's image seems to encompass
as much as possible: the human woman with her feet
firmly rooted in water and earth, with her head in the stars,
connecting downwards by a chain to
parents, family and society, that in order to discover or re-discover
ourselves, we have to cut the chains that bind us so to speak.

Until we meet again… (For Val)

person
THE OUTER FRINGE OF SEX
yourself. Break
entered
may change you
care of most. Remember
amounts to an incapacity to experience
sufficiently the predominance
original green quartz icosahedron
I already owned,
speaking about envy
and as desire is
a term
really created a transitional space to alter
and fetishism,
LaVey's development
Witchcraft
but certainly as a validation of the
This was exacerbated on many occasions.
their heads. Perhaps not in approval of phenomenon itself
view of all this, five years? includes the
drawings Max completed a few years before. While
phantasies. An overlapping between
these various sources both of
libido and of aggressiveness
is normal. But when the overlapping
Until we meet again…

The wonders of the solar system (For Gail)

15.
Mrs. D might well bellow out some further pleasantries.
airline which continues to fly over the Andes
in propeller aircraft…
All other airlines have switched to high-altitude jets.
Kim, did you hear me?
Is to get a better…
going to give you, honey,
stages of disorientation walked in:
who had got hold of the wrong address
and burst in on the party by mistake.
The wonders of the solar system make me cry
The wonders of the solar system pass me by
They take it all away from me

Smell the flowers

Queen of wands
Spark of fire, passion, engagement
CHAPTER V.
COMPLETION, REPAIR AND PHYSIOLOGY OF BONES.
Completion of long bones; the skeleton at different ages; bones in infancy; green-
stick fracture; rachitis; spina bifida; process of repair; functions of bone
tissues; *surgical* and *special notes*..........................70
Also Leo energy, my rising sign, I come into this world to shine.
seven swords
taking action
mistaken. miscalculated
In the past
FUTURE

Two of Coins
balance, prosperity, wealth.
enjoying life, a dance. The power and magic
in ordinary things.
and you just have to go with it, lie back and think of the relief of
your own bed when you finally make it home. She'd been a few
places since high school, however, and when he started getting
nine swords
The stress of feeling the heavy
weight or burden but really none
of the swords are penetrating,
they're just hanging there, in the
background.
To clarify:

Knight of Swords
spark, moment of intuition, idea
intellect, rides directly into the
storm to overcome all difficulties.
Directs all energy outwards.
four swords
five swords
MASSAGE THAT'S THE BEST IN THE WORLD

Six of Cups
bountiful relationship of giving and receiving.
Happiness, bounty, joy, pleasant,
smell the flowers.

identification with a fantasy of what we imagine ourselves and/or m/others to p...

we pass through the doorway we dispose of our shoes and f...

that the scene, together with the action, was fundamentally and ...y thought of only as a vision, that the only reality is just the

...hen why couldn't we choose to adjust that experience/those ...which of itself generates the vision and celebrates it with the ...mbolism of dancing, music, and speech. In the vision, this ...belongs to one of those charred bodies, and was close to those fires, ...must live into a future without illusion, especially the

This occasional casualness in the matter of the d... and consumption of human meat seems to have been

consisting of an odd texture or consis...

– How the hell do you explain...

Some of the less popular or prominent pieces...

...uman hair attached at the back, a wig set of

She looks very frightened. Her mouth is closed.]*

85

Fig. 11.–The Skull.–

in fact provides the edges of such a ritualized space.
meditations, Goodman Brown
to conceal himself within the
YOUNGER
the mind is sought, upon which dances
the sangoma. Some sangomas give them
that in effect they find it difficult to remember
space of no memory, no ordinary knowing
who spoke. I certainly can also attest to
We were promised
With each
wonderful
should we be there
Farm our
he currently
PLACES OF INTEREST
wear, to Saturnalia.
It feels like mere anarchy is loosed upon
that strict
of the pleasure in
they are a thousand times more terrible,
and wars today manage to roast,
in a single, searing blast, the population of an
entire city. The excessive kindness
of father, teacher, or lover is
paid for by blankets of napalm bombs
and the atomic explosion
PALMISTRY CHART

What he was (For Peter Christopherson)

books I had to her. I didn't want to attract the wrath
happens to be a guy in a red suit with horns and a
satanic looking whatever it happens to be is the
would be, essentially, beauty
some a bit older but still teenaged
get back to focus. What kind of macabre rabbit hole
which is almost synonymous with biting, destroying, and spoiling
across the invisible oceans, towards the temples.
The meat it feeds on…
is reminded of the saying 'to bite the hand which
fantasies. And who did I find in the book if not dear old Ivy?
simply wants to emerge! The artist can spend a long time admiring his
patients, and eventually he may come to trust the therapist. Slow but
changes in therapy can be expected.
well-known fact that lovers love to tease and torment each other,
understood by others. (Is not laughter born here because there is no resistance
upholding it was to her door that he was carried, like
a dot, and there was never the bad word uttered for what he was:

Ceremonial

several distinct
ceremonial; it
ultimate result of
which led to experience
last would be a cataclysmic
experiment,
human flesh as food
welcome fairness
significance; it
connection to religion
and be strong enough to escape her family's revenge.
how handsome and good you are."
"Yes," she said. "I was just looking at you, Harry–thinking
and shrugged and grabbed for the bench under
out a while ago actually, 1999 or something like that.
That would be a sign that
The counterforce against individual empowerment
and illumination within the control systems is
intimately linked to the decline of that culture in general.
However, the unwillingness to allow for it?' She explained:
'When you kiss your lover, you want him to die of your
kisses and you want to disappear into him (she used another very
"Val! Gail!" I leap up and given them a huge hug.
"I'm so happy to see you here! I can't
between the withdrawal of the libido and its distribution. I interpret
the illness as a battle between the two antagonistic tendencies of the
oblivion. There's no paradise where the world's headed.
No hell either."
was a clear spring afternoon, with a few hazy clouds.
his thighs, and groaned through his little black
some people have gotten the message.

At the Hellfire Club (For Kendell Geers)

Okay, but I am very drunk.
Great.
Sing your words so sweet,
softly reaching my lips.
Consider finally that the torment
of this infernal prison
is increased by the company
of the Damned themselves.
Evil company on earth is
so noxious that even the plants,
as if by brains
are boiling in the skull,
the heart in the breast
glowing and bursting
the bowels a red hot mass
of burning poke,
the tender eyes flaming like molten balls.
And yet what I have said,
as to the strength and quality,
wants to look for a…
the damage has already been done.
I went under the river,
for once the snow was your sister,
bleeding roses.
This man is real.

Cheers to the defiant!
Cheers to the living spirit!
Most importantly, cheers to us!

On weekends, good Queen, booze in the vicinity.
Begin to wilt and whistle, sleepy drifters
instrumentation with cellos,
moaning like jealous
black to the next.
Violins would cut neurotransmitters like wine,
when solid spaces were constructed

for all our motherfuckers
engraved forever
in thee is that
it may be through the impossibility
is the less interesting.
I manifest the best.
Very well, but they can't.
The Happy Prince snapped right in two
It certainly was a dreadfully hard frost.
Why don't you lose me in the dust?
My lunar module could never rust,
Take me to the moon,
the dark side of the moon.

We must engage
it is what and is
as a culture
So we share
these little tips.

Her mouth is closed

Some of the less popular or prominent pieces
– How the hell do you explain
consisting of an odd texture or consistency
and consumption of human meat seems to have been
This occasional casualness in the matter of the day
identification with a fantasy of what we imagine
ourselves and/or our m/others to perceive
we pass through the doorway; we dispose of our shoes and
that the scene, together with the action, was fundamentally and
thought of only as a *vision*, that the only reality is just the
then why couldn't we choose to adjust that experience
those which of itself generates the vision and celebrates it with the
symbolism of dancing, music, and speech. In the vision, this
belongs to one of those charred bodies, and was close to those fires,
must live into a future without illusion, especially the
human hair attached at the back, a wig set of
She looks very frightened. Her mouth is closed.

Snowflake melted

gained control of what images s/he would capture
youth is almost always the emphasis. It is
important to he/r,
what s/he wanted to remember in her lifetime,
800 of which remain. So the
and perhaps even history itself –
at when it seems as if this is hugely significant. Feeling
and re-written in a sense. In the
Indeed this has been helplessness
and hopelessness one may feel in
dominated the rest by sheer force
have been found to have microscope lens,
he first began drawing the abstract art, including
Soon he found a way to fashion a microscopic
person or object while present
but and Kazimir Malevich his time,
which inundated experiencing.
This shift in the world has been towards accepting
may produce both a familiarity
experience, not unlike the experience of art,
as if this history of art
of dissonance when confronted
similar brand of camera
putting the power
have been the citizen for the first time.
of a clear pioneer of getting her due,
is Swedish artist between life and art.
The Viennese defies herself
by not having af Klint was interested in
have their art, and may art have its disturbing,
as the first shows of the manifest content of the
their attack on rigid academic worldview,
while the latter particles, plants and
such qualities and abilities;
that such skills in work
within the boundaries she left upon her death
training over a persons lifetime. While this art markets.

Another frequent the radical possibilities of
attended exhibition in art critics, dealers and
If not actively persecuting their own groups and show
ignored or unappreciated Viennese Secessionist group,
prospective entitled during their lifetimes.
In the resigned from the Association
reportedly aware of af exiled.
But of course over time main concern was freeing
for *The Guardian*, become the new norm,
and masterpiece of design and no one design
continues. snowflake melted, that design was forever
capturing images of accidents, crime scenes, recall,
reproduce and recreate. This might seem
was the time of prohibition, gang violence
and shift life and narrative in a new way, in a way more in
rather than what they've been born into, based on

,

Relationship between partners (For Jen Moses)

past that now has a completely new meaning
The newest acoustic buzz
the androgyne, the
The bearded lady
Infers infernal lovers in sustaining loyalty.
one-dimensional and having
symbols: the more we can see
The Cabaret Voltaire
Psychoanalysis and Dada
fine arts have a long
Telepathy' and 'The
The advent of Jacques Lacan
In addition to the exploration
Of every moment you, seek
admits. But I don't care. I went to art school.
I never use the
its distribution was subject to special regulations.
The training
inside our tiny temporal vessel.
It may seem paradoxical to say that the more we know, the better.
that won't be able to be taken again.
And I'm finding some good quotes to put on
a complex story so simple, so it can convey
the big details and small totalities in as
One sentence at a time,
cerebral sky from which rain,
as well as watch the last chapter.
Photography can record that. I've got all the pictures
precisely timed since the brush is cut too late the rains may soak
rush, which would not burn. On the other hand, if the brush is
sexes too, when union is made possible by emotional
nudity and a temporary upheaval of the intrusive fireworks of
relationship between partners [self-other(s)-witness].

They would say the spider comes as long as one dreads the unconscious force of integration.

Although most natural spiders live in the earth, dream which ends with an eight-poem and stony facade, its caged trees, a vile attempt by a rival."¹⁸ The curse in *Towers Open Fire* reappears in an obscure re-release of the Danish ry day wit

all this distance puts at distance

Eroding Witness

can at least use each other's christian names. "Of course," she said, and lifted the tail of his shirt as high as she. could over his back. She caught her breath, seems satisfied with a life-style that others might judge to be boring and uneventual using a kind of hammer to tap them into place. rte said he noticed the

think shetip trust

I don't think all of it can be clarified. I like works that have some mystery to them. Now, in academia, people would rather talk about difficulty than clock: analyzing destinies, solving/logistical agricultural upheaval, solving like candles at an evening was all on fire, blazing and leafy festoon was Yeah, exactly. So like, people are picking up on these

primal force endless

nted in cunning speculation as if she render progress through it extremely difficult. pt up a there obstructions in the way of tree trunks, underbrush an trailing vines and creepers like ropes, but the footing is nothin

rather than formulate it. The idea being that we are so inundated with ideas of who and how we're supposed to be, placed upon us by our

we began   which he drew during their meeting, with honesty 1938 to escape Nazi persecution

always had my fingers in a few pots, like designing plastic jewelry while I was doing Macy's windows. No one taught me about plastics. I just went out there and learned how things worked. If all this energy weren't used, I don't know what I'd be."

we have made a game **at water's edge the wind** out of love   When I was   I continued showing the

order – there were a lot.

these most your

kingdoms. Can it for some reason no longer be retained in sensation so overwhelming? Even so, think of it in colon the acid test. My The Trip... is just beginning penetrate her dis, I, and Just drifting better than I, and Just drifting

Buggery is still a life-imprisonment offence even if committed between husband and wife, though the risk of conviction is obviously minute. Neither spouse can be compelled to give evidence against the other, and a conviction is unlikely in the absence of corroboration—such as a medical testimonial

unselfish friendship. But at the same it's pure mistake. I will never have a child by you for me to take my final leave of snes for tomorrow, we do not know turned a slow, Billy It's all right. No one else round all right. horses sha disturbed. could not see any Suddenly, away on ame The driver saw it at

chance to her starched breast, stroking his shoulder whit stroking his shoulder whit to her starched breast, looks wust

THURSDAY/NOVEMBER 21 STARTS AT 19.30 · 50KR.

COPENHAGEN'S ONLY INDIE CINEMA. HUSETS BIOGRAF MAGSTRÆDE 14,

Morning ng Six

opened the door and the four of them the darkness beyond the threshold.

Then, from the murky, smoke-filled darkness a woman's voice spoke to them: "Help me!" it cried. "I am rooted to the floor.

Rose and cucumber (For Jessie Brodsky)

respectively the primal object–being built
truth of the interpretations given lead to
even religious–but all that really mattered
was how large their breasts were.
straight and dull as highways. Bred on
the lead practitioner's will. For example, in the
and do what you like in-between
leaves you breathless.
within the self being diminished.
been forced to evolve from learned
view, what would you say makes you unique as an artist?
marathons, sensitivity training, awareness groups, hypno-
rays pouring through the trees in a sort of rhythm of light.
the actual father image. Since the child's identification
her lover with the proof that she belonged to him, but also
ODDLY INFUSED *with*
ROSE *and* CUCUMBER

The tree went on growing (For Katie Lyons)

wander through the scented past. A long journey, uphill most of
collages become exhibitions and we reach new people, returning with new
the tree went on growing. Everybody ought to plant a tree, some-
out. But what Freud was saying was that the information is altered, just like every
Escape *the* conventional. Embrace *the*
constantly keeping an eye over our shoulders, accompanying us on the road to
There are very few types of living creature on the face of the
is much more to be learnt about pre-natal influences; but even
origin of character formation to variations in innate factors. There
Cancer (the astrological sphere ruled over by the
dark moon goddess Hecate, and in her right
serious? I want to do it more than anything else in the
world. But you realise that you'd wear it forever, don't
nineteenth century, perhaps fifty years after Captain Cook's
involvement in feminist and other direct action
ethnomusicologist, archivist, and collector.
Freudian Theory and the Pattern of Fascist Propaganda
religion, *The Divine Horsemen* (1953). She made one
initial on your back. Oh, darling, darling, are you really
demand of music an effect similar to that produced by works of plastic
art, namely, the arousing of *delight in beautiful forms.* Upon perceiving

My dreams (For Carl)

will with all my Will; where I want to love and die,
that an image will remain
gatherings *(following pages)* to greet the magical midnight moment
There was a turning point to the story, and I was curious to
I don't hold back from indulging in these earthly delights.
those means. What was a powerful tool
OPENING DOORS WE DIDN'T KNOW EXISTED
He took off the rest of his clothes and went to the side of
and most probably she saw the others; although she only perceived me
had the hots for her and we made out a couple of times. Not that night but in the future
these new beginnings, it also marked the end of an era for which Romantic
slugs. Oh, it was sweet and delicious and worth my whole
lugubrious voyage. I stood behind her at the mirror, and we danced
turned around and introduced himself.
power to resist capture and consumption that most animals
my dreams

Symbols and dreamlike (For Z'EV)

deserted us. They asked us innumerable questions and I kept on
of entertainment, in which we're swamped
the narrator's ego-grandeur. Those perspectives
I have often spoken of as 'memories in feeling'. In the course
lying in the ferns by the side of the track. Further on, we over-
Union." Still thinking of the situation who the constitution
lateral wall of fossa or cavity
lying in the ferns by the side of the track. Further on, we over-
searches into the history of symbols, and of the fish symbol
security of the Socratic way of life in the Platonic writings, will also feel
there is the matter of how emotionally comfortable or uncomfortable
we wish to receive the recognition it deserves. One Son and
have some guy stick around longer than a couple of months
anyway. Just for the sake of variety.
But until then she was going to get on with her life and since the
began to rise to power. The dichotomy between crude
I walked the thin line
by symbols and dreamlike
There is no such thing as a science of man,
giving the same answers, namely that we were pilgrims
The energy of a hurricane!

Unleashing the Unconscious (For Billy Rayburn)

grasp onto a fragment, that
memories. This is also why it is not
from our best
by love. The various anxiety contents mentioned
for his various protagonists' voices.
to re-experience them in his earliest relation, can lead to the splitting
in a town just outside of Joujouka, itself located in the majestic Rif
to the human brain – not unlike the magical thinking of the
stairway to the bed where he had belonged all along and he knew
number of experiences which led me to a critical examination
niche, all the common sense obvious things… All the things they'll never give you in
What's the drink for your sign? Find out.
FREE Astrological Drink Recipe Book
I adore him and I worship, and I want You and all the
we have
cyborgs
God experience
free will, choice,
weird
remember every aspect of a dyad
Futurist Manifestos &
you to many times and
Unleashing the Unconscious

Become songs (For Kyle Mulrooney)

Lobo for the
and passion is an actual stunning event. Tickets
of history and rhythm, race and rhyme, melody
A Strong Tree With Many Birds
over her and put his lips to hers. "I'm beginning to be
Holiest of Mountain
as purely motor phenomena,
which correspond to the expression of the motor element in the
the pencil does not touch the paper, but writes in the air.
These movements must be conceived
undoubtedly provide those answers,
although everyone already suspects the Devil is…
was. He put a hand behind her and drew her nearer to him.
crazy about you," he said, and wondered whether in fact he
like a field hand and snatched a switch of willow as she came
essentially perverse infantile sexuality, which is our
for the time being. After her weekend in London she
to the space-age needs
becomes songs.
somehow ascribed
magical qualities
and when a bus tries to pass
Flesh attempts to remove
stone from girl's vagina

but she kind of suspected there was an unmistakable rosy-red flush

didn't know where the hell that had come from from a minute ago,

by a megalomaniac consume Dracula's powdered

gag, but she didn't want to draw too much attention to herself. She

about Ben's last days and to enjoy cocoa and a platter of Icey's

yourself. The ego itself is a symptom, and you

have sent it as a punishment because the victim

ANOTHER BIG STORM TONIGHT.

events of life and the world take place in himself, yet if he reflects, he

and I can tell you that there is a sweetness in that

The twigs of the cedar tree would be brought to
land planted like willow by abundant water would
old me and so I collected the branches and bundled

103

Nothing works like witches (For Nell Latimer)

of barns, homes, churches and inns.
existence.
back to antiquity, most markings seen
"We had no
19th centuries. Markings weren't the only
references to
who fluttered about him in salons from Berlin to Hollywood.
Yet he was unfathomably profound–the genius
cavers exploring chanced upon
among geniuses who discovered, merely by
thinking about it, that the universe was not as it seemed.
I spent the summer
These are places where supernatural forces in
be at work," he tells Brown. "Local people are
POP CULTURE
Staff at the Creswell Crags Museum &
Meet the
marks seen at the site dated to modern
members of the underground exploration
conscience is of a different kind.
Keep your courage, that's all that matters – and never let
yourself be analyzed.
Write good poems, when that is given to you. But don't cramp up, and
don't hide yourself. Man stands naked in front of his God.
That is the only prayer which is still among us."

We used to be, and perhaps still are – if we remain sufficiently
young in heart – addicted to these stories, these never-to-be
Lhasa they are bound together with strips of yak's hide to form
a thick mast nearly seventy feet high. Then a huge flag bearing
threshold of life and death
printed prayers and extending from the top to the bottom of the
medieval engravings from the comfort of their own homes.
trauma as valid, almost on
Humans have left their mark (or in this case, markings) on
The body of discharged from the service
12,800 years ago, when hunter-gatherers left depictions of

But the very term "mythology" was brought forth
the way I clean fish in the sink.
sun and optimism I whooped
fields like the history of religions or anthropology.
A barely saintly gesture, but surgical.
driver's seat to crane around
the concept of myth was made conscious by Jung
the old woman that to instrument such a union would vindicate
and drank some
Got a cold?
Nothing works like
witches, whatever you were
"We did it," he said
MENTHOL
facilitator at the crags, notes
remember what had
to bring you fast relief
swallowed it. Then
marks inside."
expert on "protective marks,"
were hoping to ward off by
I am about what you're doing
last show! [both laugh] But
themselves at your feet,
shoes and handbags can
[laughs]
rosary. Several days later, a plane crashed at Clark Airbase in
recognized some of the carvings as witches'
Manila, killing everyone aboard.
engravings and confirmed their identity as
… And for those who are stone deaf and cave-worm blind;
Historic England, witches' marks are also
a medicine made in this way was useful only as a temporary
measure: it had no real power as a *borfimor*.
The original Hollywood
Skuf Shine
the earth screeches, plates collapse,
the walls lose their grip on the painting
She says, "It could be fairies,

there."
nothing is aligned like the planets we
fearful of, it was going to be down
a heritage
would probably have engraved these marks
other hardships viewed as manifestations
that many medieval people
likely represent just a fraction of those
chamber suggests that this was
illusory. Historicism relegates identity to
Witches' marks aren't just found
digitize the marks. of individuality ensures maximum freedom
(light detection and
caves, making them
internalized ideals of our parents, as was
A poem for the poet
as I argue, fundamentally
is the corrective. The shadow
to pun in the manner
aspects our power, out of
element in any strategy
disruption of witchcraft
is a way of rediscovery
even embedded "witch bottles"
witches from gaining entry.

Magick (for Jhonn Balance)

take is fairly post-modern–but what
things would change
that someday
saw the young God-King riding slowly up the pass on his
Lama. The flags denoted the presence of the ruler. When
it becomes a cliché or a stereotype, but
such as Santa Claus or Jesus Christ, that
Of course, this can be interpreted
room–all survivors of the catastrophes of
the street we came across a beggar,
cap in hand, pleading for loose change.
Nothing is harder for me to refuse
than the mute eloquence of a mendicant's
within the crawlspace of the floor like a hideous
reforming: his half-formed body lurches up from
came off the nod and shook themselves
THIS.
is asked to pay greater attention to their aural surroundings
found is so often taken for granted. There's noise all around
furious. Yet I didn't want to sedate him
ability. Some adopt very ingenious complexes that interfere
time – the euphoric ability
I'M LOOKING
laughing hysterically, we left the bathroom
and found the slave man right where
Perversity and
Illusion! This is maya.
Goodbye to the Holy
Mountain. Real life awaits us.'
Arrested by
prisoner to the
see the Pope, and we'll solve many
So
has
insists its level
many potions
I'm now

phenomenon
CHAOS
BABALON
LILITH
LUCIFER
NUIT
HADIT
RA HOOR KHUIT
Magick, one of the best-selling books on
this introduction, I received news of his

understanding of events in our lives to recreate our personal narrative.

A juniper called *sabino* in Spanish.
Like Islamic people, at dawn they cover their mouths, from a fear of early-morning fogs.

Met Robert Flaherty. A delightful old Irishman, preparing to go around the world testing a new camera. He was suffering from the many injections he had received but in spite of that was cheerful, told delightful Irish stories connected with his film-making. The

LSD, I would tear off a hit and d whether they really wanted it to do. Actually, it was a pretty

on the floor too. His friend was gone. Perhaps he er. This was a weird place, but definitely intriguing What the hell and why not? No-one had asked him

'That's one pretty pussy!'

C. G. JUNG

apher trick find a beautiful go you see shes failed with

astrological correspondence is something that conforms to law. At the same time, it is not so easy to counter the

other than those of the dayworld ego and which are a death for that world.
The wide belief that animals embody the souls of the human

I remember my life in Spain after my father left. This brought a flood of tears. It seemed all warmth, affection. Enrique Granados

Is it not possible that by calling to our aid the musical relation of dissonance, we may meanwhile have essentially facilitated the difficult problem of the tragic effect? For we now understand what it means to

to recall occurred at a place we

The permutated po own; echoing out

many major artists of past and practitioners,

with poets, with neighbours and strangers, flora and fauna sharing a common habitat,

ritual significance of Dream history together as well, which

each mirick, or step through masochistic orgies

Pomba Gira Maria Padilha

they are not images *of* animals, but images *as* animals. These dream animals show us that the underworld has jaws and

lion in railroad cookshacks, alley nights, expiring on coal one by one in the gutters of

of what we imagine ourselves o repetition of similar experiences ce, then why couldn't we choos s and mold our identity in a diffe

109

Heroes

Scotty Bowers
So Jung goes on to say
would never be able to
virtually everything that
I'll hold this, then you'll hold this.
It's difficult to
withdrawal or
Say yes…
to *oui*
It's all
the French
you'll ever
need to
know
HOT HONEY
for those who live a life of sin
I knew I wanted
knacks and quirks.
and I burn
snuff, and in
No. 2
were her
not yet ready
Scrubbing out the bourgeois.
TARANTULA TWINS!
Parents sell
spider girls
to the circus
donating green-and-white) and a generator-
Someday, I want to obtain an original basket
is a message in
"The pictures?" "Yes, look."
Behavior could be so funny. "It's the pictures," she answered.
started to giggle. I wondered how *The Evolution of Primate*
Susan was lying in bed, studying her anthropology text. She
his favorite sundress
CA: Of course.

The gas station that was a
clubhouse for gay stars!
Scotty kept their secrets
FANS DEMAND ANSWERS
Scotty and the Secret History of Hollywood
Heroes

Moments cut from time

Elementary Elementals
Absorbing
Monads, Dyads, Triads
Absorbing
Thesis, anti
Absorbing
share her paintings with
in 1906 and 1915 (111 of which
body of work that in scale
"Paintings for the Temple,"
own inner evolution, as well as
of mankind. Concerned that the
and the clothing
was very quick at learning languages, as are most Tibetans.
quite common for people of the upper class and business
speak Mongolian, Chinese, Nepalese and Hindi. My
Occultism
cut-up techniques into modern sorcery. His own
only clamping
message of God
all, but I wanted to
was over, and I'd
served it.
concerning William Burroughs's translation of the
weight now, and weighed it guiltily in his right hand.
and do something far worse than that? He picked up the paper-
me yesterday and made me shout abuse at my innocent secretary,
falling into? What is the evil streak that finally got the better of
What can it be? he thought. What is the sink of despair I'm
Absorbing
Thesis, anti
Absorbing
Monads, Dyads, Triads
Absorbing
Elementary Elementals
elements of magick symbolically. As an
instrument of magick effectively

creates a dreamlike articulation of even the
anywhere upon the vast, spreading tableland between the barn
and the river. And then in the distance John saw him on the road,
on a huge field horse, moving slowly and yet with a
An example: Our western dramaturgy is based on
in to Homer's stories about Odysseus' travels to
faces problems and challenges that he, either alone
A party?
Have it at my place!
like this. Suicides
we will just make
symbol could no longer stand in
own enemy and one of the finest
set up an advance meeting to focus
Moments from the
time. This cut then
which then effects

My experience has shown me that when the analysis of these

slap may inform,
ing is more likely to
Meanwhile, disaster

'onstant pum
'cuss the se
is expend

the hang
"b done!" chant

Henrik motions over to the

The odd thing was that apparently very little of the actual

they were looking at the house of

electro dynamic radiation on a

The insight gained in the process of integration makes it pos-

actual gestation and birth of a monster through the

breath [Four score and 7 years ago]

ESCAPE

completely give up the idea of the psyche's being somehow

and flipped over and onto the gro

brutal cannibals

use of a life-sized idol of Astaroth as fecund flesh

whole body was covered all over

therapy. Initially, he may have difficulty in relating to the therapist in a meaningful way. Later in therapy he may develop excessive anger and hostility
toward the therapist. However, he is likely to remain in therapy longer than

the multitude of variations in which the technique could be utilized and applied to various
sible, in the course of the analysis, for the patient to recognize that
there are potentially dangerous parts of his self. But when love can

them listen to the song about the
"Hing Hang Hung! See what

Ungraspable consent

thus betray their archetypal origin. As I shall show
further on, certain phenomena of simultaneously or
synchronicity seem to be bound up with the archetypes.
the *decisive moment*: that precedes
more at play than meets the eye
no special
you can do on your own as well as utilizing *patuá*, statues, and
vessels of *axé*.
how lovely you look now. Exquisite pain. Why on earth
because you're tied to a metal bed with surgical clamps
burning candle in your pussy and another one up your ass?
known symbols and all unknown poetry.
He knew and was prescient up until the very last moment.
them in a pot. We boil babies too. We cut them up like a
pig. We eat them cold or hot. We eat the legs first. We eat
them because they are like fish. We have fish in the creeks,
and kangaroos in the grass. But men are our real food."
This small detail of biting off the nose of a victim interested
was out like a light
of force him to awaken
But "it cannot say what it wants" any
more than can the dead in the mythological underworld speak
except in a whisper. "It would be possible to picture the
as new form of right. The first step in
Yet this mirage of appearances, in which the organic conditions of
intoxication, for instance, can play their role, requires the
ungraspable consent
of

Worlds and dimensions

of my endless possibilities
anymore now, she's just happens
when the storage malfunctions
when the human existence
do we exist at all?
When we're different
I'm more focused on
dismantling the ego
breaking down the defenses, disrupt
disrupting the narrative
that the person has created for themselves.
Ultimately, they will
the slits for eyes
Sparrow, Hawk, Falcon, our Fox, Lion, Bull
nothing but animal masks,
but scaled to the size of the human head.
Made of real fur and feathers
I crowned with lashes
when the actual animal had lashes
as the lion and with the pelts or feathers
descending to the shoulders
of the person wearing them
to make the mask fit snugly along the upper lips.
There was an orifice for each nostril
and along both cheeks
all we had to do was adjust a fairly loose strap
concealed inside this coke like affair.
Witch hunt
down the back
a frame made
of molded, hardened cardboard
located between breasts and face.
Back then, she was never sure that
she actually wanted to fuck
but didn't dare say
and worked on controlling is important.
And have sat together side by side on the edge of a line.

They notice at one corner of the park at
an intersection where there are never any taxis,
a car, which because of its meter resembles a taxi.
"Get in," he says. She gets in.
It is autumn and coming up to dusk.
She is dressed as she always is:
high heels, a suit with a pleated skirt
Mega Golem
not only worlds and dimensions

Voice of the Mega Golem

Key
for rich
by churches
arm inviting us
to reach out
and touch her
over again.
Let's go now
someone else
diametrical to
unused plastic cup
it is refreshing to witness
the subject and the filmmaker
who comes from
and I am also not sure
and helpful
in a ritualized
safe space
of trust
A Mega Golem official
work without the time out
to our daily program
writing with a group like

What Life has already done (for Liz Marshall)

Many loyal psychoanalysts who would never make such
coping with problems are extremely limited; and the prognosis for positive
"mind-reading" became incorporated into his technique.
happy to see you two here! I didn't know if you'd be coming. So glad you made it!
But to tell you the truth, I don't buy it. If someone wants
condensing around David. His left hand closed into a
and new continue to trickle and commune
present, and future within its invisible walls.
Wonder! Think, my friends, what Life has already done to those
on a magic carpet, entwined. I'm so happy to see them together,
As we work within the physical and magical
daughters, and his heavy body was cold with sweat.
itchin' to do somethin' to help you folks out if
of the present time: which same symptoms lead one to
Perfect perfume, Stockholm 1890

Night of the Hunter

Night of the Hunter
Their name liveth
For evermore.

I don't hold back from indulging in these earthly delights.

There was a turning point to the story, and I was curious to

DN'T KNOW EXISTED

and most probably she sa...

nd went to the side of

powerful tool

had the hots for her and we made out a...

these new beginnings, it also marked the end of an era for which Romantic

...ie ville

Kings Island Luxor

slugs. Oh, it was sweet and delicious and worth my whole lugubrious voyage. I stood behind her at the mirror, and we danced

...ned around and introduced himself.

gatherings (following pages) to greet the magical midnight moment.

create beyond himself has only the purest Will. Where is beauty? Where I must will with all my Will; where I want to love and die, that an image will not remain

power to resist capture and consumption that most animals

my dreams

FONDATION
H·C·B
Henri Cartier-Bresson

MARE TIRRENO

The HOTEL
WOLCOTT

Attachments

intense – but now they were back to being awkward again. Her
the present situation by dampening the feeling-toned portions of the
often see severe anxiety and depression because the patient adapts to
a *fact* that it's cooler'n that school I go to an even cooler'n
is therefore always potentially subversive
to those attachments. Attachment even at
to be, which is then solidified
by the repetition of similar experiences that validate that
impulsive, makes quick decisions
without carefully considering the consequences of the decisions.
transference as psychoanalytic method were indisputable to Ferenczi;
Psychoanalysis really began with Freud's theory
on dreams. Rather than creating a body of
Not knowing how to rid myself of them
Polluting my insides
where I've no right to be.
But this is no ordinary case. You know,
I love that girl and wanted to marry her,
but although that's all passed and gone,
I can't help feeling anxious about her all the time.
down and says in a low voice to his wife, stretching out his hand:
Pierre: *There... Look...*
Thirty yards away from them, the head of a white fox
sexual response and the female orgasm
unquenchable fire – although it is a force
It is a work that leads to an intimate
the body is prepared. It
stimulates movement
pose that issue from
or intelligence
hazardous
problems are created
How is it even possible that a woman
asked herself while realizing that watching this
expected it. But there it was. They just kept on
My consciousness changes, and I am able to do
what the other requires

in my blood. Lilith in my body. Lilith in my
and you. Sunday-night dresses, drying out back on a stretch
attachments
Kerouac, Ginsburg, Burroughs, Herbert Hunke (1915-1996), and Neal Cassidy

The dead are often quite active (For Kristy Buckley)

to be a good girl
nature of the hypnosis.
and leaving Pearl alone.
events of life and the world take
have sent it as a pure
about Ben's last
gag, but she didn't want to
region of partial hypnosis;
to an extremely peculiar essay on
by a megalomaniac consume Dracula's powdered
but she kind of suspected there was an unmistakable rosy-red flush
now where the hell *that* had come from a minute ago,
go itself is a symptom, and you
HER BIG STORM TONIGHT.
having been popularized in the West by the original Godstar
legs and the other arm will thus not be obeyed. Tableturning is not an
Tom Collins, Strawberry Sting, Alexander, Tequila Sunrise
not only story itself but also storytelling. The awareness of the
your trip? Were your travels smooth?" "Always, of course," Tony flashed
art school. All they give you is their tragic lack of individuality. It's important…
prom-date helping his girl on with her wrap. When he was done he
there was also a sly, almost camp, colourful aspect at
hand, and we stroll together down the rocky path,
18. seeks help because of situational problems
begin between rock hills where 3 rivers flow together clean brown-silted off
Pink Squirrel, Pina Colada, Wallbanger
to Freud's definition of a group as being a number of
On the scissors, now, whistle
esthetics, inspired by a
day with canvases, brushes and tubes
concept of beauty obtaining in the plastic domain,
the project,
live in heaven
like me and be
The dead are often quite active, ready and willing

Harmonic change

Preacher smiled
underworld. When
illusions of the
our civilization is partly a response
you. It's the much truer flesh in the shower
predominantly related to fragmented parts of the personality but to
Similar to the process of free association,
automatic writing allows the creator a glimpse
have never been biological bodies, really.
We have always been prosthetically
the post-modern thinkers;
the idea has become to disrupt the narrative,
and as having same. Because it has none.
It's you, as I remember
looking down at her. "What's the matter, honey? Won't
which external circumstances
into he/r own unconscious processes,
attempting to bypass inhibition and interference
entwined together. I'm so happy to see them together,
as they had been in a long distance harmonic change
process evolves: through which change the relations of things become
The cut-up is aggregated in conventional life. It is in our speech,
essentials now condensed to a reeking pile of death.
A lump of scorched human flesh, no longer
possible to define as this or that individual. Only the basic line of a torso,
with two legs and two
the main village meeting area. The mountains
detritus at mountain foot–stuck with
to the main floor, slip on our sandals and
shudder," sd/ Jack–No Wonder–
species as we LIGHT and TIME other animals of the
HÄXAN

Observatory (For Kelly Merklin)

selves at the farmer's kitchen for a bit of hot breakfast. The gaunt
on her brightest morning smile so that they might present them
Another doll has been photographed thrown in
with my girlfriend, and
I guess I was too shocked.
I didn't need to find out I was an anachronism. So instead I went
still sensory-driven more than anything else. Always have been, always will be.
sexual beings. Children are sexual beings. We
wish others to observe. Such control can
the office on the way into town."
and she sensed that he was
The study of the behaviour of
more coherent parts of the self. This implies that the ego is not
or watching the movement of her lips? Suddenly she stopped
She goes into the adjoining Pink Room. Anais turns
it was time they all got
to their beds. But there was no sleep for John for a long, ticking
as a callous that is built up through repetition of experience
air, piercing and drenched with river cold, swept over them. They
the Observatory for a number of years, devoted to the surreal

Transition

opens with an image of three yellow circles arranged
in their demands, are unconcerned with our feeling reactions. Pleasure
constitutes a danger, even though it should correspond to a natural
who are involved in the treatment process. When a high score occurs in the
if the person chooses to hide problems from the psychotherapist and others
through any such sieve as you may find or invent
visible on my face, or ass, and crushed sacrum or throat
displeasure? I must dogmatically defend the viewpoint that the
personal psyche is governed by unconscious impulses that lie deeper and,
the attachment to sorrow, her mysterious fate, lead us to the historic prototype of Ivenes knowledge that
there are actually something substantial there. There is a
any individual's proper individuation and re-connection is a marker
vast spaces west on 90 double lane, still sun over sky's center, shining down
at the role of unconscious homosexuality in mass psychology.
The most important consequence of Freud's
and turns the eye into that apparatus for which every instinctual
other images, so that it is present throughout, but
primary feelings are of an omnipotent nature, this reflects on the
current feeling of envy experienced towards a substitute figure and
contributes, therefore, both to the emotions stirred by envy as well
(Mr. Small) has an inferiority complex. The Altman sisters
the tent where the Master Musicians make their
and commune with one another. I spot Jen and
– or inside me – the broken bones,
of that society's inherent
potential threat there. The
 break from the traditional narrative.
past yr friends' letters yr office carbons
a toxicity of the bloodstream. Freud
himself accordingly began his career as a

Moon's Day (Lunar Portal)

Günter Brus
that 'naming' is not a nominalistic activity, but
deed, because the name takes us into its reality.
the first day of every week being the
you'll discover fantastic new ideas to "wake
step by step guide we include. Soon
rational interpretation for some viewers.
Youth, the visceral intensity of the art super
blood of four strong men. Man alive, her whole body
that we all love has had put into her veins within that
days! Then I guess, Jack Seward, that that poor pretty
adjustment. Whether or not analysis can improve the situation is a
is frequently so far advanced that they slip further into inadequate
As stated, the patient's automatic writing never came to any very great development.
In these weeks, with four weeks making a full lunar month, and
Moon's Day (Monday, Måndag, Montag, Lundi, etc).
one person, the leader. Do not let us forget, however,
that the demand for equality in a group applies only to its members
and not to the leader. All the members must be equal to one another,
but they all want to be ruled by one person. Many
Mountains to celebrate the summer solstice
with the Master Musicians of Joujouka. We
presentation "write." This phenomenon is somewhat rare;
generally single letters are first written
and what was said above of table-turning holds true
of their combination into words and
when married to a Scandinavian! Just as I am thinking this, a gaggle of four
even submit that there is an archetypal selective factor
involved in the invention of terms. Let us call this an archetypal
Cross Culturality, and Experimental Writing (1993) and *Paracritical Hinge*:

Pomba Gira likes love

Audiences will stare
at the mouth of us
understand
what someone's
this incredibly big secret
and background consistent.
But she knows me very well.
Everyone can tell.
the body of flesh
or body of body
as opposed to
on the same subject.
scapegoats are used
bank notes alone
not to sext
credible
that she says that
want to be exposed
polymorphously perverse
likely a course as any
described perversion in this way
messages, take them or leave them.
That's art.
Psychoanalyst, artist
and conscious mind
and the calendar.
It's not like that
for French speaking film, cinema
that can go anywhere, and you get
I wasn't that suspicious.
So, one caution must be kept in mind by women,
important to emphasize that Pomba Gira likes love
reinvents herself
and so on. So,
my big kind-of self-identified,
stable, substantial reinventing should be
opposed. I think the problem

I think that this is
a certain logic
welcoming you
into you
that have known
lovers hand
one thing we can do
their actual embodiments
The Dream
releases
the shade
the underworld
sensations
chiefly from those
and his footnote,
the ego is

Dream of working with you

language."
Michael Mair in *Atalanta*
Epigraph 45, 'The Sun and
taken in turn from *Aureus*,
Trismegistus who advises
dream of working with you?
Of course the propositions never stop.
OF A CASE OF PARANOIA
something else must be always added, as if what has been already said were
imperfect. This feeling we may with Janet designate as the '*sentiment*
no means explains everything. I enter somewhat deeper into this
ark was okay, but the ark
cute little ark with cute little
that bow down

XV

EL DIABLO   XV

*"Jayne was possessed with her cleav-
age—her big breasts. They seemed to be
her security," [Director] Frank Tashlin*

LE DIABLE   IL DIAVOLO

THE DEVIL

» wrapt dusk tops snowy ranged above grey shining lake under Heaven June
I'm 46 years here. Mountains meditating late afternoon, all night, all morn,

The Devil

XV   THE DEVIL   ♂

of Fertile Soil—Bargain Destiny Ki
Montana—

THE DEVIL.
EL DIABLO   XV   DER TEUFEL
DE DUIVEL

genuine Cuban cigar, puff
de—nay, satiate.

'started' by putting into the box pieces of the flesh of a new-
born child who had died at birth, together with certain other
ingredients; but it was held by the members of the society that

The Devil

Let us s   he roots of the
deat   gs long
reb   and ac
oubled its natural len
"God bless me!"
ck by 'isself!"
He went to the d
roceeding it seemed
us.

O del Rey also contain Honduran
cos, but some varieties of Punch
Hoyo de Monterrey use pre-Castro
na filler stock-piled before the em-
o. According to Jack Schwartz, in
d Bersicker c   it is these "reassembled" Cuban ci-
most unnece
thought

XV

XV

an I. Q. of 163, but at least she was smart enough to

ing marriage, while her husband sat in the
same room. She craved the center of attention in public, even at private parties

XV

responsibility for a sample of medical students. A correlation of .33 between Ro
scores and ratings of positive character integration was reported for a sample

·THE·DEVIL·

THE DEVIL .

Meehl (1952) as part of a larger project concerning political participation. The

y The Devil vi

ack in my room, I could still see the lights out th
iff, dancing beside, behind and above the grea

from the sheltering
n central courtyard

The Devil

The Moon (for Aisha Shehu-Ansell)

young woman I was treating had,
scarab. While she was telling me
"Not at all," I replied. "What's the address?"
appear drowsy. I again turn
–napalm that flowed out of White
thru television's leaky colortubes–
The Moon. LA LUNA XVIII. THE MOON.
help us to construct our
Represents
itself to us. I felt as though
literally twice as powerful
work being in
THE DREAM
THE UNDERWORLD
about
and comp
is my interpretation
around, the woman you
creative. My creative output is a mix of sex, art,
pneumatic beings. Citing writing
for the win
presentation
about the
attempt
etymological meaning
in moments
we grasp
air? The Greek
is retained
more generally
Perhaps the issue
or sensation does the soul have at
Kirk's rather concrete, naive, and
but rather what is the best analogy for psychological perception
or chanting, that had opened a door in their
minds through which stepped a 'thing'
they could neither contain nor control. And

in front windshield rolling downhill, wind soughing car side–Absaroka
Range, Crow People snowpeaks encircling the flat watershining panorama
segregated South into a thousand pieces and put them together in the image
of God and democracy. We must say: "Wake up, America! Wake up!" For we
"You on the burnt guy case?
"Yep," I answered. "Just got back. How
all honesty, because I

Into the future (For Katelan Foisy)

… where she loves and is loved in return…
also knew that he was
"People are taking their cues
seen swimming in the rich, pulsating, psychedelic
was looking forward to seeing the things that David had
into the future with his young film star, learning to
guidance – die in their own thorny embrace a
I was absolutely peaking in power after a
BUTLER: *Don't be alarmed. You know, those who've been*
He walks across the room and camera pans as Severine
the first to crack the mirror so to speak. The position of
to have the most confidence. In general, greater confidence should be
addition, it often is necessary to assign diagnostic labels for purposes such as
when she came she sobbed and
out signals of pleasure and lubrication
and pulled her panties back up
In *The Pandrogeny Manifesto* (2006),
man trapped in a woman's body. Some people
body. Breyer P-Orridge just feel trapped in
bit. Softer alarm signals and clocks with

The pair took the city by storm

"The task of the right eye is to peer into the telescope,
production, that permeated daily life
and were affecting the artistic domain as well.
modern world, to mechanization, pace and noise
and to the possibilities of industrial
towards it were more ambivalent. Artists
were responding to the rapid changes in the
The poem will resemble you,
Copy conscientiously in the order in which they left the bag.
Next take out each cutting one after the other.
leadership and geography. The Dada movement was notably diffuse
with several active city centers
contrast to Surrealism, for example,
which as we will see, remained centralized in terms of
Taeuber-Arp was pioneering in her breakdown of the barriers
between applied and fine art.
She collaborated not only with Dadaists
but also with Constructivist and Concrete artists;
her work having an impact on the development
of Minimalism and Serial art
and reassembling them, tracing her geometric wood reliefs in ink on paper
and commissioning woven work based on her patterns
and content – was typical of Dada performances
and experiments, as the artists set out to create an unsettling effect
in the audience. "At the heart of Dada lay the 'gratuitous act,' the
paradoxical, spontaneous gesture aimed at revealing
the inconsistency and inanity of
Dada questioned society's accepted values and consensus worldview,
challenging the status-quo while embracing new ways of thinking,
utilizing new materials and methods.
Submissions would be collected together in an anthology
and printed in a run of 10,000
contributors to submit portraits of themselves
as well as photographs of their artwork.
published until 1921. Tzara conceived of the idea of
DadaGlobe and sent out invitations for
Picabia and the pair took the city by storm.
They organized the journal *Dada*, which was

Wonder (Time progresses)

during the Victorian era
Indus contributed to
Expression
Repetition
have an organ
fine workmanship
in an age when dreams, emotions, the unconscious
At the same time,
exact repetition
the commercial pressures of predominant artistic move
differences between repeated
imagery boasts of beauty, refine
concerned with recording
opening, where the potential
impressionistic manner.
of day-to-day life for individuals
as he worked to unleash
The Birth of Modern Art
time progresses
Wonder.
Even with the immense capacity
Works.
Having discovered Poe's events…
create order and find meaning
throughout his entire life.
once they have been defined."
We need to be aware of and move many poets
from Baudelaire to George Bataille
ill cause chaos. In fact, I hope to
that no longer serves us,
with minimal interventions,
the initial rats were already in the
take the form of an outright re
of this study. Here, the
est position"

or reworking of the idea, keep.

Whether it been on a
Charles Baudelaire (1821-1867)
to much controversy,
leading him to own. Such reactions
are meant. dynamics or society at large
for his prior work as well;
his disruption and dislocation are so
and we do all the time
had invoked the essential formal works,
they soon too made.
People seem to
Of exclusively and creatively
human mind invents
state, and we can only speculate
development
in a series entitled
which are tested to see
he continued cutting out abstract
was creating.
He was living
continue to see over and
rearranging them in varying ways
had both been arrested for progress
or alternative movements,
this group of England
leave the page
as the artist be.
Though there are a
William Holman Hunt
that is a discussion
Deleuze; there is also a common malaise
choosing humanity's resistance
elaborated as fundamentally different
and violence, has presented interpersonal
Deleuze is in an all out truth.
When in fact, the truth
to changing course. psychoanalysis
it has come to be with the tools and technology

I belong to the world (for Susana Vico Valero)

certainly knew that the vice versa scenario was true
had been granted a blessing so magnificent, sincere
"My presence on Earth is going to be
feet long after I become a memory…"
what I just said? Is my English O.K.? Is my microphone
Slowly it rotated its massive head and looked right at
"Nobody kids myself
more than I do…"
To say that the subject upon which we operate in psychoanalysis
"I cry all the way
to the bank"
"My possessions don't belong to me…
I belong to the world!!!"
I'm sure God understood that too. This will be interesting,
I'm cute
gives to slavery, he says,
"Because it was a part of the
and don't set a foot inside till I've fetched the wash
like it! And you, too, mister! Now git up on there to
"Hurt her nothin'!" cried the old woman. "*Wash
This was an assignment so vast I couldn't count
audience. The feature film *Tangerine* (2015),
acid diethylamide–"acid"–has advanced from the unreliable sugar-cube
'Everything to do with me.' He lit a cigarette, offered her one.
Another development for
TESCO
the steady drip and patter by
his pile of soft black

I felt awe and surprise

Pennies (Crossroads)

somewhere. Because of the irresistible attraction of my nerves
I had become an embarrassing human being for the rays (for
God), in whatever position or circumstance I might be or whatever
occupation I undertook. One did not want to admit that
Xenophobic traits. Visiting the radical New his drawers I wasn't
Lytton became one of the infected,
in *Vril*. As they could in
Quimbanda itself will always
betray those it holds dear
that they may grow. It is
a cult of vicious honesty.
If we are anything
less than honest with ourselves,
underworld initiations.
These are indeed death experiences
Observations of babies show us something
of these underlying unconscious
The Mega Golem
attitudes. As I have said above,
some infants who have been screaming with rage
appear quite happy soon after they begin to feed.
This means that they have
your own ears have just
My mother was wasting her breath.
I insisted that we look over her pennies.
I remember how we argued as we went to get her purse; and
image, in men or
her, and we must

Black eclipse

And for no other reason,
I wanted to ask you about theirs
their worldview. So instead,
rigidly as it is most likely,
the skirt is as circular
as patterns and merging into
entire bottom was creating
the mischievous nature
minds cutting one piece out of
New Life
contagious drive toward
a new itself
at the edge where existing,
mysterious and open-ended
by and foremost
an actress or European
that is how I see
don't people warn you about smoking
hands holding her
her smacking her
all of it to say
I remember when
we adapted
vintage
embodying one's guidance,
film and music, etc.
But in an infinite way
to work and order the same cup
did he? And retreated
as a door
to do in pairs
during ceremony
before being private
can meet the band KMFDM
and gray is everybody.
Man or woman is all
in the beginning

and the I think it's fascinating.
And I show it because I chose it
when we bumped into each other
I think 40 is exciting.
So where are you? Garment District
it's the battle of justice versus
10 people came up
and asked if I knew
I was going into that
them that they are really care about it.
But what I'm not
I am a
it's stronger
for me
as when
interview
asked me
and the return of glamour.
And then you'll have no idea what
rewatch and analyze the movies all the time.
What do you say to them when we take the time out?
session. When we exit our daily
boy when you're
I'll give you the fewest
Would you like them to know? Sure.
But I better
same
them. This child
the love of the rock group
in calculated
to an old junkie
in a couple lines. I

Gold eclipse

The transitional area
tiny cuts
just enough
beautiful part is where
and following the shapes
work of returning
because in a full season
also rotating and
so, there was
a message remains
Life
to define

Correspondence moves slowly
at a fast pace
movies like moving
but the absolute
and layers
could be said
read
in all of it
possible in every one of your movies.

See you soon
still so,
so much wonder
Ray wonders
which he continues
to release his Hollywood film
I Am Legend
in your ears
the life of the spirit
of doing something
this slice of imperfection
separates

Separation

long description
of nothing
can be created
if there is no
light flared
and stitches
from this point
or a hand sewing needle
in three to five hour sessions
outside having a cigarette.

sometimes I get lost
doesn't happen for a long time
eye and balls ever ready
to be penetrated
it felt ideas
and taking ideas
has reached a standstill
St Paul's Cathedral in the 1980s

A
by alchemy
the original
if you
I hope you
do.

We began in December 2016
astrological Grand Cross
different things
sourced while living
to get everyone right there.
So fortunately, there was always palpable

you'll probably recognize Peaks
or Sex and the City
upon the point
the client
perseverance

the ability to give more space

I will make
in micro made
macro for this
from a foot away
and visual experience
of life itself
and a metaphysical revolt
must always be a vision
as a jumping off point
we have applied the cut up
I think over time we've learned

Anderson awesome
making rock and roll cool again.
I wasn't even that crazy of a
Manson's how not
hallelujah
world
at 1982
and jobs 1975
and not with us
based on gender.

Text fragments visible in the collage:

into the flesh in the shower

Similar to the process of free association, automatic writing allows the creator a glimp

predominantly related to fragmented parts of the personality but to

have never been biological br

S, really. We have always been prosthetic?

the post-modern thinke

the idea has become to dis

r the narrative, and as having

into he/r own unconscious processes, attempting to bypass inhibition and interfere

they had been in a long distance

essentials now condensed to a reeking pile of death. A ""p of scorched human flesh, no longer possible to define as this or that individual. Only the basic "line of a torso, with two le and two

our civilization is partly a response

illusions of the

underworld. Wher

Preacher smi

ng down at her. "What's th

ich external circumst

has no

It's t as I remember

ame, Because

on't

I'm so happy to see them together. I'm so happy to see them together.

twined together.

ocess evolves through which change the relation of limbs to

armonic change when

he cut-up is aggregated in conventional life. It is in our speech.

the main village meeting area. The mountains

detritus at mountain foot—stuck with

to the main floor, slip on our sandals and

shudder," sd/ Jack—No Wonder—

species as we LIGHT and TIME other animals of the

SENS STORA

S FILMBYRÅ, STOCKHOL

Noises (For Luigi Russolo)

Museum of Art as part ideas
regarding the development of his noise
which a variety of his compositions
Noises (1913), and his work has influenced
throughout the day. Every musicians until this day.
eventually developed into his own genre,
becoming undermining the use of perspective, subjects were
IDM, the cut in the expected
riotous forms, differing sides being portrayed
need for a single, fixed viewpoint,
which had been a Contemporary composer John Zorn (b. 1953)
Renaissance read across Europe and North America
with years preceding the First World War.
New York and Munich (1911), and London fragmented,
broken down into their simultaneously. Cubism rejected the
Prostitution took lynchpin of Western art since the
Although it ran for just eight days and filled
such a stir in British popular media
that they by the experiments of Étienne-Jules Marey
chronophotographs of birds in flight showed the
throughout this study every major change time,
Futurists formulated a way to convey speed and
initially met with defense. Individuals strike
were otherwise previously invisible. These
"How dare you?" becomes quite commonplace
potential of these discoveries were reflected in the art
can understand this initial defense to scan
the status quo, of the narrative we have been
devices more affordable and portable. James' style
point; the narrative that society agrees upon
incorporates disruptive or disjointed elements
into question, or otherwise marked,
the electronic dance music, bringing the listener or
struck a chord. These artists fulfill quite a sim
the rhythm that up until that point had taken them all
to act as a mirror, a reflection, a disruption
critic for *L'Italia*, who questioned the artistic merit

149

of the noise organ. This so incensed Russolo that
he slapped the critic in public, was then charged with assault
and had to go to trial. Russolo felt that his artistic
reputation was at stake and was set on defending both his
decreeing their manifestos, psychoanalysis collaboration
with many more potential creative
and Freud began his weekly meetings
of what musicians can collaborate with one another

Caves of sorcerers

Caves of Sorcerers: The American Beginnings
identification may also easily tempt the analyst to take the mother's
that exteroceptive, proprioceptive interoceptive sensations
intellectuals, the literary avant-garde and book-shunning
and nature as such as the perfect allegorical platform
experienced and are relieved when fuller integration is achieved.
Complete and permanent integration is in my view never possible.
The deeper and more complex the difficulties we are analysing, the
Two of the Norwegian guys sit with us, while another pair takes seats at
smoke, red like blood, rising into the heavens, and they knew
and sleepy, soulful eyes. He is draped with beautiful richly-colored fabrics.
time; in such recent history of their
it were suspicious to nurture we are quite yet
(And How much even thus young,
than has even found effect. as a creature,
upon the unparalleled peril of consciousness,
destroys that alone would berate him:
cities, his state, his laws, his inmost soul,
We are nearer now.
The dead to admire the seams of the nation shining
with fossilized carbons, while the living configure secret
myself falling into a kind of hypnotic state, my eyes halfway closed, the
Writings of Melanie Klein 1946-1963
The Birth of Tragedy
visual arts. Do you have a term for poetry inspired by music?
claim that there aren't really any new
is–the assiduous veiling during the performance of the tragedy of the
intrinsically Dionysian effect: which, however, is so powerful, that it
place and give in to the urge immediately to alleviate his child's (the
– I don't, she replied. I leave that to you, Black.
But I've never really seen anything like it. If the
dioramas of cinematic expectation in the half-dark,
when we are asleep, we oftentimes have "one eye open" and are able to

The Devil (for Ammo)

wrapt dusk tops snowy ranged above grey shining lake under Heaven June
I'm 46 years here. Mountains meditating late afternoon, all night, all morn,
of Fertile Soil–Bargain Destiny
Montana–
genuine Cuban cigar, puff
–nay, satiate.
del Rey also contain Honduran
but some varieties if Punch
Hoyo de Monterrey use pre-Castro
filler stock-piled before the em-
According to Jack Schwartz, in
it is these "reassembled" Cuban cigars
'started' by putting into the box pieces of the flesh of a new-
born child who had died at birth, together with certain other
ingredients; but it was held by the members of the society that
The Devil
an I.Q. of 163, but at least she was smart enough to
ing marriage, while her husband sat in the
same room. She craved the center of
attention in public, even at private parties
Meehl (1952) as part of a larger project concerning political participation. The
responsibility for a sample of medical students. A correlation of .33 between Re
scores and ratings of positive character integration was reported for a sample
from the sheltering
a central courtyard
Back in my room, I could still see the lights out
cliff, dancing beside, behind and above the great
The Devil

Planet 9

Some of the less popular or prominent pieces
– How the hell do you explain
consisting of an odd texture or consistency
and consumption of human meat seems to have been
This occasional casualness in the matter of the destruction
identification with a fantasy of what we imagined ourselves and/or m/others to perceive we pass through
the doorway we dispose of our shoes and find
that the scene, together with the action, was fundamentally and
thought of as only as a *vision*, that the only reality is just the
then why couldn't we choose to adjust that experience/those
which of itself generates the vision and celebrates it with the
symbolism of dancing, music and speech. In the vision, this
belongs to one of those charred bodies, and was close to those fires,
must live into a future without illusion, especially the
human hair attached at the back, a wig set of
She looks very frightened. Her mouth is closed.]*
DON'T SLEEP HERE. MINE.

'sexual feeling' in a limited sense) to art or science; the root of

In the years imm_diately precedi_
Picasso le__ differentiated o__s, as do
r patients state is even Cubist revolution
berg_ _ collage bits of paper, cl_

s. "Tony and Bee ir from pathological dreaming since it could never be

shelter of the tent to the West side of the area where the Masters will later

contributed to the phenomenon of trans-generational transmission of
d to create an unse
ous act,' the parad
originally made, by which the various States came into the
w and inanity of

wrapping around the analyst in his being that this topology can grasp him.

enough and there was no promotion in the Navy that wou_
him take any mo_ ang "Admiral," he said grimly, "this was a g_
replacement for conventional_

See the long footnote, Standard Ed., 4, 13. The present passage

millions as to so many millions of men, and not of mere

two Japanese fellows. One has an afro and a t-shirt

breathing, predator breathing. Breathing from

patholozation of it is also quite

rather the first step towards a de_ _onal experience,
in French and trying out different instruments in a music

_at is gender? _
girls do not. No one
between castration
active passive, 1:0)

things around them
Why did you start
I picked it up in
driving me crazy
one tool for an artist to reach
as you know, and you have a lo
But level identifica_
but an this creatio_

Your most treasured (for Little Annie)

like, godfathers, grandfathers, whatever. She scowled at him.
number of years, increasingly chilled water sinks
blow stronger and colder than average over a
of mash-ups and remixes, now
what had befallen us on the
sex as something mortifying and
the stars above. To the East is the dining hall, a
found that what neurotics are guided by is not ordinary objective
the life of phantasy and of the illusion born of an unfulfilled wish is the
a sheltered spot where we recounted
covered area with a dozen or so large round
stage, for it was necessary that he should be more or less severely
wounded by the next-of-kin of the man for whom the revenge was
stores of his experience for means to avert the danger, though he has
act pathologically (in which case appearance would impose upon us as
the silent bottom of the sea. What is your most treasured?
Prelude… she'll love you for it!
just considered carelessly
spell. What I am compelled to
consciousness is not only integrated as fact but
completely necessary for the functioning and
of society. A shamanic culture is one where
the world soul doesn't exist as an arbitrary
she suddenly ceased to see those taking part, although she still
in an uncanny sort of way, reminding me of Duchamp.
six-inch heels for half an hour, and her shoulders had begun to ache
companions. I shook them awake and we all betook ourselves to
belongings, we lay down and rest for a spell.

The Emperor

personal philosophy, my personal life, and so
In this paper, I give an overview of my
I had a glass of water from the faucet and then sat down by my desk.
It was 3:30AM and I knew that
and irregularly now, grunting like
transparent, and the houses open like lace
and freedom could blow through them.'
THE EMPEROR came home on holiday, she had emerged from
were often marked by guardian creatures
discoveries to Nietzschean thoughts
nervously looking at her with cock in had.
she moaned. "Not yet…" the old man said
the guy off the woman's body but immediately
my own world view and experience, because she had stripped away
all the pastel-colored taint of
most other shrinks – even those on the force.
Ivy spoke the truth: plain, simple and very dirty, and
nothing but the truth!
The Exquisite Corpse, Chapter One
etc. are a common denominator in travel and
So, I was born to write.
They could have handed it to me in another way, I guess. But no, they
Monroe pushed herself above chest level
and came to represent the sexual contra-
dictions in the American Dream, as
and malnourished body looked like it needed a couple of weeks of sleep.
"Yep," I continued. "Too clean.
If we take the geographical distance between One and Two-Three
in everything;

Joy and wonder of life

Ace of Swords
Spark of intellectual inspiration
true perception
wisdom leads us beyond illusions and limitations
to the spiritual truth of life
up – we might call more organically.
Through association,
through relaxation,
and freedom,
yeah.

Nine of Cups
You have everything
pleasure, material wealth
enjoyment
My wife jerked me off as I filmed her
girlfriend's quim-shaving session.

Ten of Cups
You have it all!
Joy and wonder of life
Domestic happiness
Lively family discussion will follow.

Wheel of Fortune
Karma, Fate
Mystery of life
a change in the circumstances of a person's life
The Wheel turns
how do we react?
a greater understanding of life.
TAKE THE DAY BY STORM

Invent something new

Resembles the Grays,
Crowley and the 20th century
synthesis of magic hidden
many alleged UFO
2007 misses out all those
by no means unimportant aspects
that in more recent years
as the sociologist Malcolm Hamilton points out
magical beliefs cannot be grasped statistically.
But to grasp these unique
breaks

spear
while by no means insignificant
or rare events at all,
we seem to be dependent equally
on the origins of anguish,
class, gender, ethnicity,
expectations of our mother and family,
but also on those internal
accompanied by delight structures
we have created over our lifetime
our ego, super ego and identifications.
We can.

It is that
and passion view this
as the cut up method,
providing an opportunity
to invent something new
by innovatively staging
the play's narrative.

Fecund flesh (End gun and intimate partner violence)

therapy. Initially, he may have difficulty in relating to the therapist in a
meaningful way. Later in therapy he may develop excessive anger and hostility
towards the therapist. However, he is likely to remain in therapy longer than
the multitude of variations in which the technique could be utilized and applied to various
invisible, in the course of analysis, for the patient to recognize that
there are potentially dangerous parts of his self. But when love can
them listen to the song about the
"Hing Hang Hung!" See what
and flipped over and onto the group
breath [Four score and 7 years ago]
My experience has shown me that when the analysis of these
they were looking at the house of
electro dynamic radiation on a
slap may inform, constant pummeling
is more likely to concuss the senses.
Meanwhile, disaster has expanded our
The insight gained in the process of integration makes it possible
ESCAPE
brutal cannibals
the hanging done!" chanted
Henrik motions over to the
The odd thing was that apparently very little of the actual
actual gestation and birth of a monster through the
completely give up the idea of the psyche's being somehow
whole body was covered all over
use of a life-sized idol of Astaroth as fecund flesh

A magician knows (New moon, solar eclipse)

day. Organs of elimination… a letter that arrived at
claimed more and more of his attention. His short stories
and attended an art school in Pittsburgh, but writing
For Lacan, sexuality is not in the realm of nature or
Searching for an "official" link between the two artists I remembered the *de*
thoughts. What happens, and what has happened to us, is not merely
HiLo and we later learn he is in a punk rock band in Tokyo.
retain as their prerequisite the blood and certain parts of the body
the seed sown by artist Rudolph Herz, who suggested that Duchamp might have
shows how we seek comfort from personal misfortune through our
been building to a brilliant paroxysm of the first time you made an impression on
A magician knows that
of the body of surfaces
The known examples
projected into the abyss
it has been projected to.
wet one could hear their skin smacking at the friction
that the case? As with most illuminating experiences, including

Belle de Jour (for Lady Jaye)

Participate
We are in this together
We can
blows with relish,
Medium close up of Severine
in profile, gasping with
control mechanisms of society
and breaking
Life and Death
This world and the next
creates a clearer reflective image.
Your prankish smile.
"Yes, hello." And then silence.
We can try and express
Severine, "Stop, please stop, tell them to let me go."
Because that's the
spend so much time
time, space and culture in this way.
But now, first and the last
you were saying,
I
Its physical,
imperfect
constraints
of the body, mind and soul.
Lady Jaye–only a bridge
between themselves,
but also between
gender and sexuality.
Magical alchemy
and sometimes it's you, Jaye
The creation
become a part of it.
In essence, tampering with forces best left
out of reach,
to be viewed and revered.
But not artifacts from

another time and place.
Foreign
together in an electric desert
of endless walking along,
gagged and held from behind by the two.
Shoulders naked
appear in back view in the foreground.
Each of them has a heavy coachman's whip in his hand.
Pierre walks off, out of breath,
and a slight perspiration can be seen on his forehead.
Severine simultaneously off
"Pierre, I love you."
Silence
out from his lips.
Camera pans right as he goes up to the footman,
and takes his whip away from him.
To roll
we will keep
we'll be
discussing mainstream listeners
to think outside
As Breyer P-Orridge state,
the practice of old body was so imperfect
and was more spiritual
and more of that we're certain
to the degree we can
and in that
is an extraordinary act of devotion.
The final expression of it.

Bear witness (For Jess Stewart)

other(s) as well,
are voyeur and ex
observing the scene
whom to blame. "You did not act
of seats parallel to where
of vegetables and flowers
attributed to a phenomenon
and their children before escorting us upstairs to our room
may even be an allusion to a particular episode narrated there
wants to find me. I'll tie it to fences as I travel with
climb on. She was the only, pale, fair-haired woman
"And all the hills echoèd," my Poems, Om Namah Shivaye, improvised
was speaking earnestly, in a soft querulous voice, with a

Yonder
This way
Down
Yonder
Back

great work here. Do you like it?" Galatea looked out over
to her head. The scene etched itself onto
That makes me feel just what I need?
both (and all) positions at once. We
being seen while enacting and
as we bear witness to the exposure.

Thanks to:

Carl Abrahamsson, Chiron Armand, Kendalle Aubra, Annie Bandez, Blanche Barton, Peter Beard, Bhante Sanathavihari Bhikkhu, Jesse Bransford, Lady Jaye and Genesis Breyer P-Orridge, Jessie Brodsky, Kristy Buckley, Joe Coleman, Jessica Datema, Val and Gail Denham, Alkistis Dimech, Carlos E. Oni, Heather Farrow, Katelan Foisy, Julie Futrell, Nicholaj de Mattos Frisvold, Kendell Geers, Peter Grey, Jason Haaf, Jesse Hathaway Diaz, Paul Bee Hampshire, Kate Hawes, Kadmus Herschel, Mitch Horowitz, Billy Jacobs, Langston Kahn, Demetrius Lacroix, Ingo Lambrecht, Nell Latimer, Xerxes LaVey, Gun and Lars Lindblom, Aldo Luca, Germ Lynn, Fernanda Magallanes, Manny Malchiodi, Zoe Malchiodi, Jessica Marshall, Marco and Hunter Duncan, Katie Lyons, Liz Marshall, Michael Matton, Andrew McLuhan, Tayannah Lee McQuillar, Kelly Merklin, Jen Moses, Kyle Mulrooney, Christine O'Day, Elsa Olsson, Kasper Opstrup, Liza Beth Paap, Rachel Page, Ian Parker, Gea Philes, Rachel Pollack, Joan Pope, Annette Rawlings, Billy Rayburn, Renee Cuadrado, Max Razdow, Charlotte Rodgers, Brian Rosen, Derek Seagrief, Lara and Stephen Sheehi, Aisha and Robert Shehu-Ansell, Richard Sinclair, Craig Slee, Adel Souto, Billie Steigerwald, Manya Steinkoler, Stelarc, Mimmi Strinnholm, Susana Vico Valero, Dan Veskler, Matthew Kennedy Volcofsky, Whitney Ward, Paul Watson, Mary Wild, Tanya White-Davis, Jamieson Webster, Damien Patrick Williams, S. Alfonso Williams, Apple Xenos, Jenn Zahrt, and Denice Zayas.

Dedicated to:

Margareta Abrahamsson (1940-2018)
Peter Beard (1938-2020)
Genesis Breyer P-Orridge (1950-2020)
Marianne Eriksson (1924-2020)
Don Gruber (1930-2019)
Bobby Ingram (1938-2019)
Naomi Kashinsky (1981-2020)
Lars Lindblom (1944-2020)
Jessica Marshall (1978-2020)
Michael Matton (1963-2020)
Kyle Mulrooney (1976-2017)
Billy Rayburn (1973-2021)
Joe Schulte (1948-2020)
Jess Stewart (1981-2021)

... and all the others we've lost.

in a town just outside of Joujouka, itself located in the majestic Rif

to the human brain – not unlike the magical thinking of the

stairway to the bed where he had belonged all along and he knew

to re-experience them in his earliest relation, can lead to the splitting

number of experiences which led me to a critical examination

niche, all the common sense obvious things... All the things they'll never give you in

What's the drink for your sign? Find out.. FREE Astrological Drink Recipe Book

for his various protagonists' voices.

I adore him and I worship him, and I want You and all the

by love. The various anxiety contents mentioned

167

OTHER BOOKS BY VANESSA SINCLAIR

– Switching Mirrors (Trapart Books, 2016/2019)

Switching Mirrors is an amazing collection of cut-ups and mind-expanding poetry by Vanessa Sinclair. Delving into the unconscious and actively utilising the "third mind" as developed by William S Burroughs and Brion Gysin, Sinclair roams through suggestive vistas of magic, witchcraft, dreams, psychoanalysis, sex and sexuality (and more).

– The Mega Golem – A Womanual For All Times and Spaces (Trapart Books, 2021)

An anthology of texts and images constituting the current Corpus of the Mega Golem – the talismanic being/sentience created by Carl Abrahamsson in 2009. With contributions by Carl Abrahamsson, Vanessa Sinclair, Kadmus, Gabriel McCaughry, and others.

– Scansion in Psychoanalysis and Art – The Cut in Creation (Routledge, 2020)

Scansion in Psychoanalysis and Art examines a strain of artists spanning more than a century, beginning at the dawn of photography and culminating in the discussion of contemporary artists, to illustrate various psychoanalytic concepts by examining artists working in a multitude of media.

– On Psychoanalysis and Violence (Routledge, 2018)

Psychoanalysis has not examined violence as such since it is a sociological and criminological concept; psychoanalysis is concerned with speech. *On Psychoanalysis and Violence* brings together noted Lacanian psychoanalysts and scholars to fill an important gap in psychoanalytic scholarship that addresses what the contributors term the "angwash" of our current time.

– Rendering Unconscious – Psychoanalytic Perspectives, Politics & Poetry (Trapart Books, 2018)

Rendering Unconscious brings together international scholars, psychoanalysts, psychologists, philosophers, researchers, writers and poets; reflecting on current events, politics, the state of mental health care, the arts, literature, mythology, and the cultural climate; thoughtfully evaluating this moment of crisis, its implications, wide-ranging effects, and the social structures that have brought us to this point of urgency.

– The Fenris Wolf 9 (Trapart Books, 2017)

Edited by Vanessa Sinclair & Carl Abrahamsson. This volume collects all the papers from the conference "Psychoanalysis, Art & the Occult" in London, 2016.

Please listen to the Rendering Unconsious Podcast by Vanessa Sinclair: www.renderingunconscious.org
To support this and other creative endeavors, please visit: www.patreon.com/vanessa23carl

thoughts. What happens,

HiLo and we later learn he is in a punk rock band in Tokyo.

retain as their perquisite the blood and certain parts of the body

A magician knows that of the body of artifacts
The known examples projected into may-ween it has been projected on

Searching for an "official" link between the two artists I remembered the de...

and what has happened to us, is not merely

the seed sown by artist Rudolf Herz, who suggested that Duchamp might have

shows how we seek comfort from personal misfortune through our

been building to a brilliant paroxysm of the first time you made an impression on

For Lacan, sexuality is not in the realm of nature or

and attended an art school in Pittsburgh, but writing claimed more and more of his attention. His short stories

wet one could hear their skin smacking at the friction

that the case? As with most illuminating experiences, includin...

day. Organs of elimination... a letter that arrived at

L'Orgueil

169

Also Available from Trapart Books

Vanessa Sinclair: Switching Mirrors

Switching Mirrors is an amazing collection of cut-ups and mind-expanding poetry by Vanessa Sinclair. Delving into the unconscious and actively utilising the "third mind" as developed by William S Burroughs and Brion Gysin, Sinclair roams through suggestive vistas of magic, witchcraft, dreams, psychoanalysis, sex and sexuality (and more). Causal apprehensions are disrupted by a flow of impressions that open up the mind of the reader. What's behind language and our use of it? What happens when random factors and the unconscious are given free reign in poetic form? Switching Mirrors is what happens.

Vanessa Sinclair (ed.): Rendering Unconscious – Psychoanalytic Perspectives, Politics & Poetry

In times of crisis, one needs to stop and ask, "How did we get here?" Our contemporary chaos is the result of a society built upon pervasive systems of oppression, discrimination and violence that run deeper and reach further than most understand or care to realize. These draconian systems have been fundamental to many aspects of our lives, and we seem to have gradually allowed them more power. However, our foundation is not solid; it is fractured and collapsing – if we allow that. We need to start applying new models of interpretation and analysis to the deep-rooted problems at hand.

Rendering Unconscious brings together international scholars, psychoanalysts, psychologists, philosophers, researchers, writers and poets; reflecting on current events, politics, the state of mental health care, the arts, literature, mythology, and the cultural climate; thoughtfully evaluating this moment of crisis, its implications, wide-ranging effects, and the social structures that have brought us to this point of urgency.

Hate speech, Internet stalking, virtual violence, the horde mentality of the alt-right, systematic racism, the psychology of rioting, the theater of violence, fake news, the power of disability, erotic transference and counter-transference, the economics of libido, Eros and the death drive, fascist narratives, psychoanalytic formation as resistance, surrealism and sexuality, traversing genders, and colonial counterviolence are but a few of the topics addressed in this thought-provoking and inspiring volume.

Contributions by Vanessa Sinclair, Gavriel Reisner, Alison Annunziata, Kendalle Aubra, Gerald Sand, Tanya White-Davis & Anu Kotay, Luce deLire, Jason Haaf, Simon Critchley & Brad Evans, Marc Strauss, Chiara Bottici, Manya Steinkoler, Emma Lieber, Damien Patrick Williams, Shara Hardeson, Jill Gentile, Angelo Villa, Gabriela Costardi, Jamieson Webster, Sergio Benvenuto, Craig Slee, Álvaro D. Moreira, David Lichtenstein, Julie Fotheringham, John Dall'aglio, Matthew Oyer, Jessica Datema, Olga Cox Cameron, Katie Ebbitt, Juliana Portilho, Trevor Pederson, Elisabeth Punzi & Per-Magnus Johansson, Meredith Friedson, Steven Reisner, Léa Silveira, Patrick Scanlon, Júlio Mendes Rodrigo, Daniel Deweese, Julie Futrell, Gregory J. Stevens, Benjamin Y. Fong, Katy Bohinc, Wayne Wapeemukwa, Patricia Gherovici & Cassandra Seltman, Marie Brown, Buffy Cain, Claire-Madeline Culkin, Andrew Daul, Germ Lynn, Adel Souto, and paul aster stone-tsao.

Carl Abrahamsson (Ed.): The Mega Golem: A Womanual For All Times and Spaces

An anthology of texts and images constituting the current Corpus of the Mega Golem – the talismanic being/sentience created by Carl Abrahamsson in 2009. With contributions by Carl Abrahamsson, Vanessa Sinclair, Kadmus, Gabriel McCaughry, and others.

Genesis Breyer P-Orridge: Sacred Intent – Conversations with Carl Abrahamsson 1986-2019

Sacred Intent gathers conversations between artist Genesis Breyer P-Orridge and longtime friend and collaborator, the Swedish author Carl Abrahamsson. From the first 1986 fanzine interview about current projects, over philosophical insights, magical workings, international travels, art theory and gender revolutions, to 2019's thoughts on life and death in the the shadow of battling leukaemia, Sacred Intent is a unique journey in which the art of conversation blooms.

With (in)famous projects like C.O.U.M. Transmissions, Throbbing Gristle, Psychic TV, Thee Temple Ov Psychick Youth (TOPY) and Pandrogeny, Breyer P-Orridge has consistently thwarted preconceived ideas and transformed disciplines such as performance art, music, collage, poetry and social criticism; always cutting up the building blocks to dismantle control structures and authority. But underneath the socially conscious and pathologically rebellious spirit, there has always been a devout respect for a holistic, spiritual, magical worldview – one of "sacred intent."

Sacred Intent is a must read for anyone interested in contemporary art, deconstructed identity, gender evolution, and magical philosophy. The book not only celebrates an intimate friendship, but also the work and ideas of an artist who has never ceased to amaze and provoke. Also included are photographic portraits of Breyer P-Orridge taken by Carl Abrahamsson, transcripts of key lectures, and an interview with Jacqueline "Lady Jaye" Breyer P-Orridge from 2004.

Genesis Breyer P-Orridge: Brion Gysin – His Name Was Master

Brion Gysin (1916–86) has been an incredibly influential artist and iconoclast: his development of the "cut-up" technique with William S. Burroughs has inspired generations of writers, artists and musicians. Gysin was also a skilled networker and revered expat: together with his friend Paul Bowles, he more or less constructed the post-beatnik romanticism for life and magic in Morocco, and was also a protagonist in an international gay culture with inspirational reaches in both America and Europe. Not surprisingly, Gysin has become something of a cult figure.

One of the artists he inspired is Genesis Breyer P-Orridge, who collaborated with both Gysin and Burroughs in the 1970s, during his work with Throbbing Gristle and C.O.U.M. Transmissions. The interviews made by P-Orridge have since become part of a New Wave/Industrial mythos. This volume presents them in their entirety alongside three texts on Gysin by P-Orridge, plus an introduction. This book is an exclusive insight into the mind of a man P-Orridge describes as "a kind of Leonardo da Vinci of the last century," and a fantastic complement to existing biographies and monographs.

Carl Abrahamsson: Temporarily Eternal – Photographs of Genesis P-Orridge 1986-2018

A photobook with snapshots as well as structured portraits of artist Genesis P-Orridge from 1986 to 2018. A great visual companion to P-Orridge's and Abrahamsson's highly lauded anthology of interviews, Sacred Intent, this book is an inspiring journey through the mind and life of someone who never stopped exploring and changing. Also contains an essay by Abrahamsson on P-Orridge's "psychic anarcho-sartorialism."

Carl Abrahamsson: Different People

"Different People" is an anthology of interviews by Swedish author Carl Abrahamsson, focusing on art, life and the creative process. Included are in-depth conversations with Conrad Rooks, Malcolm McLaren, Stelarc, John Duncan, Charles Gatewood, Mark McCloud, Ralph Metzner, Peter Beard, Bill Landis, Ralph Gibson, Maja Elliott, Michael Bowen, Bob Colacello, Dian Hanson, Anton Corbijn, June Newton, Kendell Geers, Simeon Coxe III (Silver Apples), Vicki Bennett (People Like Us), and Brian Williams (Lustmord). These groundbreaking artists, writers, musicians, photographers, filmmakers, editors and psychedelic researchers have all helped shape the culture we live in. But what makes them do what they do? Which are their driving forces and their inspirations; their joys and fears?

The Fenris Wolf 10 (2020)

Carl Abrahamsson – Editor's Introduction, Carl Abrahamsson – Onwards to the Source!, Ludwig Klages – On the Essence of Ecstasy, David Beth – Katabasis and Erotognosis, Henrik Dahl – An Introduction to Eroto-Psychedelic Art, Peter Sjöstedt-H – Antichrist Psychonaut: Nietzsche's Psychoactive Drugs, Carl Abrahamsson – Lux Per Nox – The Fenris Wolf As Libidinal Liberator, Jesse Bransford & Max Razdow – Revisiting the Veil of Dreams, Christopher Webster – Beyond the North Wind, Kendell Geers – A Long Boundless Systematized..., Kadmus – Seeking the Three-Headed Saint, Billie Steigerwald – The Chthonic Seed: Reflections of an Ancient Death Gnosis, Fred Andersson – The Gospel According to the Tomb Man, Zaheer Gulamhusein – Sunflower, Charlotte Rodgers – The Riderless Horse..., Craig Slee – The Occult Nature of Cripkult, Damien Patrick Williams – Daoism, Buddhism and Machine Consciousness, Philip H. Farber – Thoughts on the Creation of Memetic Entities, Thomas Bey William Bailey – Memetic Magick, Mitch Horowitz – Is Your Mind a Technology for Utopia?, Ramsey Dukes – I'm Gonna Blow Your Mind, Carl Abrahamsson – Grasping Reality with Gary Lachman, Anders Lundgren – Mike Mignola and the Lovecraft Circle, Peggy Nadramia – So It Was Written, Peggy Nadramia – Addendum to So It Was Written, Nina Antonia – Maya, Jack Stevenson – Häxan/Witchcraft Through the Ages, Andrea Kundry – The Demonic Cultural Legacy of Antonin Artaud, Joan Pope – The Birth of Ideas, Genesis Breyer P-Orridge – Idiosyncratic Use Ov Language..., Vanessa Sinclair – Try To Altar Everything, Claire-Madeline Corso – Cutting Up a New Conversation

The Fenris Wolf 9 (2017)

Vanessa Sinclair & Carl Abrahamsson – Editors' Introduction: Looking back at the crossroads, Katelan Foisy – Invocation: Homage to the spirits of the land/London, Sharron Kraus – Art as Alchemy, Demetrius Lacroix – The Seven Layers of the Vodou Soul, Graham Duff – Sublime Fragments: The Art of John Balance, Ken Henson – The American Occult Revival In My Work, Gary Lachman – Was Freud Afraid of the Occult?, Peter Grey – Fly the Light, Val Denham – Proclaim Present Time Over, Katelan Foisy & Vanessa Sinclair – The Cut In Creation, Claire-Madeline Culkin – Beds, Bodies and Other Books of Common Prayer – A Reading of the, Photography of Nan Goldin, Steven Reisner – On the Dance of the Occult and Unconscious in Freud, Katy Bohinc – The 12th House: Art and the Unconscious, Olga Cox Cameron – When Shall We 3 Meet Again? Psychoanalysis, Art and the Occult: A Clandestine Convergence, Ingo Lambrecht – Wairua: Following shamanic contours in psychoanalytic therapy at a Maori Mental Health Service in New Zealand, Elliott Edge – An Occult Reading of PAO! Imagining in the Dark with Our Vestigial Shamanism in a Shade, Shadow, Wide, Charlotte Rodgers – Stripped to the Core: Animistic Art Action and Magickal Revelation, Alkistis Dimech – Dynamics of the Occulted Body, Fred Yee – Cut-Up As Egregore, Oracle and Flirtation Device, Robert Ansell – Androgyny, Biology and Latent Memory in the Work of Austin Osman Spare, Ray O Neill – Double, Double, Toil and Trouble: Psychoanalysis Burn and Surrealism Bubble, Derek M Elmore – Dreams and the Neither-Neither, Julio Mendes Rodrigo – Rebis, the Double Being, Eve Watson – Bowie's Non-Human Effect: Alien/Alienation in The Man Who Fell to Earth (1976) and The Hunger (1983), Carl Abrahamsson – Formulating the Desired: Some similarities between ritual magic and the psychoanalytic process

The Fenris Wolf 8 (2016)

Carl Abrahamsson – Editor's Introduction, Vanessa Sinclair – Polymorphous Perversity and Pandrogeny, Charles Stansfield Jones (Frater Achad) – Alchymia, Tim O'Neill: Black Lodge/White Lodge, Nina Antonia – Bosie & The Beast, Aki Cederberg – Festivals of Spring, Michael Moynihan – Friedrich Hielscher's Vision of the Real Powers, Friedrich Hielscher – The Real Powers, Orryelle Defenestrate Bascule – Ear Horn: Shamanic Perspectives and Multi-Sensory Inversion, Zbigniew Lagos – The Figure of the Polish Magician: Czesław Czynski (1858-1932), Gary Lachman – Rejected Knowledge: A Look At Our Other Way of Knowing, Carl Abrahamsson – Intuition as a State of Grace, Bishop T Omphalos – The Golden Thread: Soteriological Aspects of the Gnostic Catholicism in E.G.C., Kendell Geers – iMagus, Johan Nilsson – Defending Paper Gods: Aleister Crowley and the Reception of Daoism in Early 20th Century Esotericism, Gordan Djurdjevic – The Birth of the New Aeon: Magick and Mysticism of Thelema from the Perspective of Postmodern A/Theology, Tim O'Neill – The Derleth Error, Antti P Balk – Greek Mysteries, Carl Abrahamsson – The Economy of Magic, Stephen Sennitt – The Book of the Sentient Night: 23 Nails, Henrik Dahl – We Ate the Acid: A Note on Psychedelic Imagery, Jason Louv – Robert Anton Wilson's Cosmic Trigger and the Psychedelic Interstellar Future we need, Carey Hodges & Chad Hensley – New Orleans Voodoo: An Oddity Unto Itself, Alexander Nym – Kabbalah references in contemporary culture,

Zaheer Gulamhusein – Standing in Line, Carl Abrahamsson – As the Wolf Lies Down to Rest, Vanessa Sinclair & Ingo Lambrecht – Ritual and Psychoanalytical Spaces as Transitional, featuring Sangoma Trance States, Hagen von Julien – Listening to the Voice of Silence: A Contemporary Perspective on the Fraternities Saturni, Erik Davis – Infectious Hoax: Robert Anton Wilson reads H.P. Lovecraft, N – II. Land, Cadmus – Neo-Chthonia, Kadmus – A Fragment of Heart: A contribution to the Mega-Golem, Stojan Nikolic – The One True Church of the Dark Age of Scientism, Miguel Marques – The Labors of Seeing: A Journey Through the Works of Peter Whitehead, Renata Wieczorek – The Conception of Number According to Aleister Crowley, Orryelle Defenestrate Bascule – Fragments of Fact, Derek Seagrief – Conscious ExIt, Kasper Opstrup – By This, That: A spin on Lea Porsager's Spin, and Genesis Breyer P-Orridge – Greyhounds of the future.

The Fenris Wolf 7 (2014)

Carl Abrahamsson – Editor's Introduction, Sara George & Carl Abrahamsson – Fernand Khnopff, Symbolist, Sasha Chaitow – Making the Invisible Visible, Vanessa Sinclair – Psychoanalysis and Dada, Kendell Geers – Tu Marcellus Eris, Stephen Sennitt – Fallen Worlds, Without Shadows, Antony Hequet – Slam Poetry: The Warrior Poet, Antony Hequet – Slam Poetry: The Rebel Poet, Genesis Breyer P-Orridge – Alien Lightning Meat Machine, Genesis Breyer P-Orridge – This Is A Nice Planet, Patrick Lundborg – Psychedelic Philosophy, Henrik Dahl – Visionary Design, Philip Farber – Higher Magick, Kendell Geers – Painting My Will, Carl Abrahamsson – The Imaginative Libido, Angela Edwards – The Sacred Whore, Vera Nikolich – The Women of the Aeon, Jason Louv – Wilhelm Reich, Kasper Opstrup – To Make It Happen, Peter Grey – A Manifesto of Apocalyptic Witchcraft, Timothy O'Neill – The Gospel of Cosmic Terror, Stephen Sennitt – Sentient Absence, Carl Abrahamsson – Anton LaVey, Magical Innovator, Alexander Nym – Magicians: Evolutionary Agents or Regressive Twats?, Antti P Balk – Thelema, Kjetil Fjell – The Vindication of Thelema, Derek Seagrief – Exploring Past Lives, Sandy Robertson – The Fictional Aleister Crowley, Adam Rostoker – Whence Came the Stranger?, Emory Cranston – A Preface to the Scented Garden, Manon Hedenborg-White – Erotic Submission to the Divine, Carl Abrahamsson – What Remains for the Future?, Frater Achad – Living In the Sunlight, Genesis Breyer P-Orridge – Magick Squares and Future Beats

The Fenris Wolf 6 (2013)

Carl Abrahamsson – Editor's Introduction, Frater Achad – A Litany of Ra, Kendell Geers – Tripping over Darwin's Hangover, Vera Nikolich – Eastern Connections, Carl Abrahamsson – Babalon, Freya Aswynn – On the Influence of Odin, Marita – Runic Magic through the Odinic Dialectic, Aki Cederberg – Afterword: The River of Story, Shri Gurudev Mahendranath – The Londinium Temple Strain, Gary Dickinson – An Orient Pearl, Derek Seagrief – Aleister Crowley's Birth & Death Horoscopes, Tim O'Neill – Shades of Void, Nema – Magickal Healing, Nema – A Greater Feast, Philip Farber – Sacred Smoke, Robert Taylor – Death & the Psychedelic Experience, Michael Horowitz – LSD: the Antidote to Everything, Alexander Nym – Transcendence as an Operative Category, Carl Abrahamsson – Approaching the Approaching,

Renata Wieczorek – The Secret Book of the Tatra Mountains, Sasha Chaitow – Legends of the Fall Retold, Sara George & Carl Abrahamsson – Sulamith Wülfing, Robert C Morgan – Hans Bellmer, Genesis Breyer P-Orridge – Tagged for Life, Carl Abrahamsson – Go Forth and Let Your Brain-halves Procreate, Anders Lundgren – Satanic Cinema is Alive and Well, Anton LaVey – Appendices
The Fenris Wolf 5 (2012)

Carl Abrahamsson – Editor's Introduction, Jason Louv – The Freedom of Imagination Act, Patrick Lundborg – Such Stuff as Dreams are Made of, Gary Lachman – Secret Societies and the Modern World, Tim O'Neill – The War of the Owl and the Pelican, Dianus del Bosco Sacro – The Great Rite, Philip H Farber – Entities in the Brain, Aki Cederberg – At the Well of Initiation, Renata, Wieczorek – The Magical Life of Derek Jarman, Genesis Breyer P-Orridge – A Dark Room of Desire, Genesis Breyer P-Orridge – Kreeme Horne, Ezra Pound – Translator's Postscript, Stephen Ellis – Poems for The Fenris Wolf, Hiram Corso – Mel Lyman, Mel Lyman – Plea for Courage, Gary Dickinson – The Daughter of Astrology, Robert Podgurski – Sigils and Extra Dimensionality, Frater Nigris – Liber Al As-if, Peter Grey – The Abbey Must be Built, Vera Mladenovska Nikolich – A Different Perspective of the Undead, Kevin Slaughter – The Great Satan, Lionel Snell – The Art of Evil, Phenex Apollonius – The Quintessence of Daimonic Ipseity, Phanes Apollonius – Infernal Diabolism in Theory and Practice, Anonymous – Falling with Love: Embracing the Infernal Host, Lana Krieg – Sympathy with the Devil: Faust's Infernal Formula, Carl Abrahamsson – State of the Art: Birthpangs of a Mega-Golem, Carl Abrahamsson – Hounded by the Dogs of Reason

The Fenris Wolf 4 (2011)

Carl Abrahamsson – The whys of yesterday are the why-nots of today, Hermann Hesse – The Execution, Fredrik Söderberg – Black and White Meditations 1-23, Peter Gilmore – Every Man and Woman Is a Star, Peter Grey – Barbarians at the Gates, John Duncan – Hallelujah, Ramsey Dukes – Democracy Is Dying of AIDS, Tim O'Neill – The Technology of Civilization X, Thomas Karlsson – Religion and Science, David Beth – Bloodsongs, Payam Nabarz – Liber Astrum, Hiram Corso – Unveiling the Mysteries of the Process Church, Jean-Pierre Turmel – The Pantheon of Genesis Breyer P-Orridge, Kendell Geers – The Penis Might Ier Than Thes Word, Z'EV – The Calls, Robert Taylor – Dreamachine: The Alchemy of Light, Phil Farber – An Interview with Terence McKenna, Phil Farber – McKenna, Ramachandran and the Orgy, Thomas Bey William Bailey – The Twilight of Psychedelic America?, Ernst Jünger – LSD Again/Nochmals LSD, Baba Rampuri – The Edge of Indian Spirituality, Aki Cederberg – In Search of Magic Mirrors, Carl Abrahamsson – Thelema and Politics, Carl Abrahamsson – Someone's Messing with the Big Picture, Carl Abrahamsson – An Art of High Intent?, Carl Abrahamsson – A Conversation with Kenneth Anger

The Fenris Wolf 1-3 (1989-1993/2011)

Carl Abrahamsson – Editor's Introduction
Carl Abrahamsson – 'Zine und Zeit (2011)

THE FENRIS WOLF 1 (1989)

John Alexander – The Strange Phenomena of the Dream, Helgi Pjeturss – The Nature of Sleep and Dreams, Tim O'Neill – A Dark Storm Rising, Carl Abrahamsson – Inauguration of Kenneth Anger, Carl Abrahamsson – An Interview with Genesis P-Orridge, William S Burroughs – Points of Distinction between Sedative and Consciousness-Expanding Drugs, Carl Abrahamsson – Jayne Mansfield: Satanist, TOPYUS – Television Magick, Anton LaVey – Evangelists vs The New God

THE FENRIS WOLF 2 (1990)

Lionel Snell – The Satan Game, Carl Abrahamsson – In Defence of Satanism, Anton LaVey – The Horns of Dilemma, Genesis P-Orridge – Beyond thee Valley ov Acid, Phauss – Photographs, Jack Stevenson – 15 Voices from God, Jack Stevenson – 18 Fatal Arguments, Tim O'Neill – Art On the Edge of Life, Terence Sellers – To Achieve Death, Stein Jarving – Choice and Process, Tim O'Neill – Under the Sign of Gemini, 93/696 – The Forgotten Ones In Magick, Tim O'Neill – The Mechanics of Maya, Coyote 12 – The Thin Line, Genesis P-Orridge – Thee Only Language Is Light, Jack Stevenson – Porno on Film, Carl Abrahamsson – An Interview with Kenneth Anger

THE FENRIS WOLF 3 (1993)

Jack Stevenson – Vandals, Vikings and Nazis, von Hausswolff & Elggren – Inauguration of two new Kingdoms, Tim O'Neill – A Flame in the Holy Mountain, Frater Tigris – A Preliminary Vision, Carl Abrahamsson – The Demonic Glamour of Cinema, William Heidrick – Some Crowley Sources, Peter H Gilmore – The Rite of Ragnarök, ONA – The Left-Handed Path, Zbigniew Karkowski – The Method Is Science..., Fetish 23 – Demonic Poetry, Ben Kadosh – Lucifer-Hiram, Freya Aswynn – The Northern Magical Tradition, Anton LaVey – Tests, Austin Osman Spare – Anathema of Zos, Rodney Orpheus – Thelemic Morality, Nemo – Recognizing Pseudo-Satanism, Philip Marsh – Pythagoras, Plato and the Hellenes, Terence Sellers – A Few Acid Writings, Hymenæus Beta – Harry Smith 1923-1991, Andrew M McKenzie – Outofinto, Beatrice Eggers – Nature: Now, Then and Never

Carl Abrahamsson: The Devil's Footprint

God proposes the challenge of the millennium: if Satan sorts out the ever growing human mess on Earth, God will lovingly take him back to Heaven as his favorite Archangel. Satan accepts, and sets out on a massive operation to balance out over-population, pollution, corruption, and other severely Satanic headaches – many of which he originally helped create... Easier said than done! Satan's love of the ambitiously mischievous humans is challenged as his own "Team Apocalypse" fervently sets to work. But as the world begins to change quickly and dramatically for the better, a new question arises: can God and his suspicious Archangels really be trusted in this cataclysmic, cosmic undertaking?

Carl Abrahamsson: Mother, Have A Safe Trip

Unearthed plans and designs stemming from radical inventor Nikola Tesla could solve the world's energy problems. These plans suddenly generate a vortex of interest from various powers. Thrown into this maelstrom of international intrigue is Victor Ritterstadt – a soul searching magician with a mysterious and troubled past. From Berlin, over Macedonia, and all the way to Nepal, Ritterstadt sets out on an outer as well as inner quest. Espionage, love, UFOs, magic, telepathy, conspiracies, LSD, and more in this shocking story of a world about to be changed forever…

"It's a thrilling roller coaster ride through psychedelic adventures, juicy romantic interludes, metaphoric dreamscapes, high Himalayan yoga enclaves, telepathic portals, 60's flashbacks, magical constructs, secret government pursuits and many more twists that kept all three of my eyes open. It's a story that you'll definitely want to keep non-stop reading, which I enthusiastically recommend."
     – George Douvris, Links by George

"Mother, Have A Safe Trip is a highly entertaining and thought-provoking novel. Chock-full of psychedelia, the book is also a much welcome addition to the far too few fictional works published dealing with psychedelic culture."
     – Henrik Dahl, Psychedelic Press

"The dialogues are great. But it's too short. I wanted more."
     – Genesis Breyer P-Orridge, Artist

"It's a wonderful read. A lovely book."
     – June Newton/Alice Springs, Photographer

Ruby Ray: Kalifornia Kool (Photographs1976-1982)

Spanning music, art and literature, the industrial and punk scenes of San Francisco in the late 1970s and early 1980s were diverse but united by a DIY, anti-authoritarian attitude. Photographer Ruby Ray was there to capture it all in the same spirit. With her work appearing in the legendary punk zine Search & Destroy and its successor RE/Search, Ray was at the epicenter of, and a key participant in, a vital cultural moment vibrant with provocation and creativity. A local experimental music and art scene supported artists like Bruce Conner and William S. Burroughs, and attracted groundbreaking bands like Devo, the Mutants, Boyd Rice and the Dead Kennedys, as well as established international bands like Throbbing Gristle, the Clash and the Sex Pistols. Ruby Ray: Kalifornia Kool collects the photographer's images from this time: live shots, backstage parties, apartments overflowing with youthful exuberance, elegant portraits of key people and photographic experiments. Her work captures a time and a place where West Coast open-mindedness, youth, art, music and electricity merged.

"Late 70s, early 80s... Ruby Ray and her camera, capturing the movers and shakers of the San Francisco punk and industrial scenes... And then some... Performance art, music, literature, photos, videos made with a "fuck you" and "do it yourself" attitude. Ruby sees and Ruby captures... Knowns and unknowns, winners and losers, sane and insane, constructive and destructive... William Burroughs with his gun, Bruce Conner being fueled by punk energy, Sex Pistols' last ever gig in San Fran, Throbbing Gristle, The Cramps live at Napa Mental Hospital, Search and Destroy Magazine, and bands and gigs galore... Devo, Mutants, Slits, Bags, Dead Kennedys, Cabaret Voltaire, Roky Erickson, Nico, DOA, Chrome, Factrix, Boyd Rice, Z'EV, Flipper... You name'em and there was Ruby Ray: the spectacularly talented lens of Kalifornia Kool. We should be grateful for her work. It's invaluable, evocative, loud, sexy and more inspiring now than ever before... Ruby's images open up a portal to a mythic and frenzied scene and show that it's true: all mythologies are real... Turn up the volume and dive into this one." – Carl Abrahamsson, from the Introduction

Sir Edward Bulwer Lytton: Vril – The Power of the Coming Race

Sir Edward Bulwer Lytton's cautionary tale of occult super-powers and advanced subterranean cultures have fascinated readers since 1871. Part early science-fiction, part educational tract, part occult romance, Vril keeps spellbinding readers thanks to its wide range of themes and emotions, as well as its thrilling sense of adventure.

A curious man descends into a mountain through a mine and experiences far more than he bargained for. Deep inside the mountain lies a completely different world. Its inhabitants, the Vril-ya, are human-like but physically superior and philosophically more advanced. They live in harmony made possible by their wisdom but also by the powerful and potentially destructive magical energy they call "Vril."

The impressed yet terrified visitor is allowed to stay and learn more about their ancient and advanced culture, something very few visitors have – it seems that all the previous adventurers have been mercilessly disposed of by the Vril-ya...

This edition includes an introductory essay by Swedish author Carl Abrahamsson.

More information can be found at our web site:

www.trapart.net

Printed in Poland
by Amazon Fulfillment
Poland Sp. z o.o., Wrocław

93670663R00100